THE UTOPIA
OF SIR THOMAS MORE

Plan of Utopia, from the Edition published in Basle in 1518

The Utopia
OF SIR THOMAS MORE
including Roper's LIFE OF MORE

and LETTERS OF MORE AND

HIS DAUGHTER MARGARET

MODERNIZED TEXTS, WITH

NOTES AND INTRODUCTION

BY MILDRED CAMPBELL

Published for the Classics Club ® by

WALTER J. BLACK, INC · ROSLYN, N. Y.

Manufactured in the United States of America
by H. Wolff, New York
Designed by Stefan Salter

Contents

53,024

Contents

Introduction

NEW SOCIAL and political ideas are part and parcel of
the thinking of our time. The decades following World War I
produced a crop of them; and the aftermath of World War II
with its even greater dislocations, material and spiritual, promises another. Hence a recent American radio broadcast discussing a social program that called for a six-hour day and depicted
the good life as one in which there were no inequalities of wealth
can scarcely have startled the casual listener. He may, however,
have been surprised to learn that the author of the theories under
discussion was not one of his contemporaries, but a sixteenth-
century Englishman, Thomas More, whose *Utopia* was first
published in 1516.

Its appearance on a radio program marks the most recent
effort to bring More's work to public attention, but it was one
of his own friends, the famous French scholar, William Budé,
who first pointed out the quality of the *Utopia* that was likely
to give it permanence. "Our age," he wrote, "and future ages
will have this history as a precious source . . . which each one
may take and adapt to the use of his own state." Budé spoke with
insight. Within five years the *Utopia* had been published in as
many different countries in Europe and had gone through seven
Latin editions. During the four centuries since that time it has
been translated into seven languages and there have been many

editions. The present modernized version of the first Elizabethan translation, with much of its original flavor still intact, will, it is hoped, make this classic accessible to a still wider group.

It is often said of Thomas More, as of Francis Bacon and other men of insight and vision, that he was ahead of his time; just as Shakespeare and those whose works have a quality of universality are said to belong to all time. There is surely truth in both statements. But how quickly every Bacon scholar learns that there are acts and words of his which can be understood only in the light of the ideas and practices common to his particular world. And replete as are the plays of Shakespeare with observations and truths that transcend any one age or place, they contain also many a line that could scarcely have been written by anybody but an Elizabethan Englishman. Never yet, one ventures to say, was there a man completely divorced from his own times. Certainly Thomas More was not. The very fact that he had ideas that were in advance of the practices of his day— and some that might still be labeled advanced—is but a case in point. For nothing was more typical of the young intellectuals of More's time than their stock of advanced ideas. One will do well then before reading the *Utopia* to take some account of the environment which produced it.

In More's age, the age of the Renaissance, educated classes of all Western Europe, who enjoyed the common intellectual heritage of the Middle Ages, were participating along common lines in new adventures of the mind and spirit. It is significant that the *Utopia* in Latin was published in six great European cities before it came out in London; and that Germans, Italians, and French were reading it in their own tongues before it was translated into More's native English. In some respects it was a time not unlike our own, particularly in the spirit of curiosity that it displayed, its eagerness to push forward the boundaries of human experience, and to unlock the secrets of the universe. Indeed there had been a good deal of this spirit abroad in Western Europe since the twelfth century, and it grew apace.

In 1491, about the time that More entered Oxford, a young Polish student, Nicolaus Copernicus, began his study of mathematics and astronomy at the ancient University of Cracow. Though later to take degrees in both law and medicine, his heart remained in the astronomical studies which he pursued more or less as a hobby. The result of the hobby was in time a new conception of the universe. In the same spirit, if in many instances less fruitfully, others were carrying on scientific observations and initiating experiments. As in the age of the Enlightenment, two centuries later, it became something of a fad for young intellectuals to dabble in science. One of the most pleasing glimpses we get of More's relations with Henry VIII, whose youthful delight in learning endeared him to all scholars, is of the two closeted in the King's private rooms, discussing astronomy and geometry, or climbing at night to the roof of the palace where Henry led More, "there to consider with him the diversity, course, motions, and other operations of the stars and planets." One can see how it pleased More's fancy to have the Utopians "very expert and cunning" in astronomical matters, devising instruments with which to comprehend the sun and the moon, "and all the other stars which appear in their horizon."

The theoretical aspects of scientific study were being illumined by the knowledge and speculative thought of the Greeks; for unlike our own contemporaries, More and his friends sought to replenish the streams of their thinking from the wellsprings of the past. Medieval scholars had never been as completely out of touch with classical sources as is sometimes imagined, and in the fourteenth and fifteenth centuries, Italian humanists brought more treasures of the ancient Greek world, in particular Platonic philosophy and science, into the knowledge of all Western Europe. Northern scholars traveled to Italy to learn Greek and steep themselves in the classical learning which, poured into new molds, became the New Learning of their age. An even greater stimulus to scientific development on the practical side stemmed from the Arabic lore that late medieval scholars had introduced to Western Europe.

By More's time the new printing presses had made all of this knowledge far more accessible than it had been before. The speed with which the *Utopia* became generally known within so brief a time after it was written would have been impossible even two generations before. The career of John Holywood's astronomy book is another example of the power of this invention. Holywood, a Yorkshireman of the thirteenth century, had prepared his book largely from an Arabian treatise. It was copied by hand a good many times by medieval scholars, but in 1472 it was printed by one of the new presses in Ferrara. By 1500 it had gone through twenty editions and within the next half century reached its sixtieth printing, a testimony both to the effect of the printing press and the popularity of scientific studies. The Utopians, it is interesting to note, were so impressed with the report brought to them of the printing press that they had in a short time contrived one of their own.

Advances made by the European scholars in astronomy soon came into play in the field of navigation, and maritime equipment was improved to meet the demands of commercial enterprise. On the southwest tip of Portugal in the fifteenth century, the research laboratories set up by Prince Henry the Navigator had developed into a veritable school of navigation. Spanish and Portuguese engineers trained there prepared the way for Columbus and the other explorers whose discoveries were to fire the imagination of Europeans for generations to come.

More's countrymen, like those of other northern nations, were, in the main, behindhand in these activities at first; but the French and Dutch would soon be busy. And the time was not far off when stories of English sailor lads, recounted in taverns and alehouses throughout the land, or set down in books by men like Richard Hakluyt, would put such an itch for the New World into English blood that there would be no stopping them. Even the interim between the Cabots' voyages in 1497 and 1498 and those of the Elizabethans, Frobisher and Drake, was not the complete gap that the history books sometimes make it. The exploits of the Cabots, father and son, were still making good talk among the seafaring folk of Bristol, and well-informed Englishmen were reading accounts of the voyages of their

southern neighbors. In fact, the New Found Lands were a subject of conversation in the More household at the very time
that the *Utopia* was under way. William Rastell, More's versa-
tile brother-in-law, fostered a New World enterprise, which apparently included plans for both exploration and colonization.
Thomas More and his father helped to finance the project, and
the expedition set out in 1516, six months after the *Utopia* was
published. It was destined to failure almost before it got started,
chiefly because of a mutiny on shipboard. How many such ex-
peditions were dreamed of, how many actually undertaken, it
is impossible to say. The failures do not get written up. But the
New World was growing in men's consciousness.

It was not strange, therefore, that Amerigo Vespucci's account
of his *Four Voyages,* first published in Italy in 1507, and "now
abroad in every man's hands," should suggest itself as perfect
material out of which to fashion a foundation for the ideal
commonwealth that was growing in More's mind. A fictitious
framework with enough basis in fact to enhance its credibility
was a favorite device of Renaissance scholars, as it had been of
the ancients. According to Vespucci's own statement, he had on
his fourth voyage left behind him twenty-four men with arms
and six months' provisions, that they might explore further
the islands of the western seas. To identify one of these with
Raphael Hythloday, the sun-tanned mariner whom More en-
countered in conversation with his friend Peter Giles on a
street in Antwerp, was merely to take advantage of a timely subject and situation.

Another aspect of contemporary life with implications that

were to affect the *Utopia* was the tremendous increase in wealth. Commercial activity, to which the discoveries and explorations were an added stimulus, was going forward on an unprecedented scale. An expanding economy had many benefits to bestow, but, as More was aware, not all of its effects were beneficial; nor did everyone share in its bounty. Increased metal reserves became available near the end of the fifteenth century, after something of a shortage a generation or so earlier. These, along with the malpractice in currency manipulation that kings and their ministers indulged in, and an increased demand for goods of all kinds, were producing an upswing in prices that eventually brought ruinous dislocations to the social and economic systems of nearly every country in Europe. Its effects in England were especially bad, as will later be apparent; and everywhere these disturbances added to the complexities of international relations, already strained to the breaking point by commercial rivalry and royal ambitions.

The growth of the national state under a strong monarchy was the most characteristic feature of the political development of the early sixteenth century. The term "power politics" had not yet been coined, but all the practices to which it applies were rife. Francis I of France, Henry VIII of England, and Charles V, King of Spain and after 1519 also Holy Roman Emperor, were the Great Powers, with the Pope on occasion one of the group. Every trick and blandishment, honorable or dishonorable, was practiced among them in the effort of each to best the other and strengthen his own power. Diplomacy had become the chief game of kings and ministers. And dozens of smaller potentates,

INTRODUCTION

German princes and heads of Italian city states, aped the Great Powers and engaged in activities no less open to question.

More was to learn at first hand of the ways of nations with each other. In 1515, he was sent on his first diplomatic mission to Flanders, to negotiate new commercial agreements for the benefit of English mercantile interests. He began writing the *Utopia* while on this trip and nothing is more truly reflected in its pages than the author's concern with the state of international politics and the problems of nations learning to get along together. Another mission to Calais followed in 1517, this time to negotiate with the French merchants. And as a member of the King's Council, More was present in 1520 at the Field of the Cloth of Gold where the kings of England and France, meeting in the midst of gorgeous pageantry, made promises that neither of them kept.

Governments sought to foster a warlike spirit among their peoples. Feats of arms were glorified, and kings asked no better means of settling their disputes than war. Common folk were not asked what they thought about it, and men of distinction like More and Erasmus, who hated war, were almost alone in their protest. Hence it was that the Utopians who detested war and belittled military glory went "contrary to the custom of almost all other nations. They were not, however, complete pacifists. War in Utopia was held to be justifiable when fought in self-defense against an invader; or in support of friends whose lands were overrun; or for the deliverance of those who were oppressed by tyrants; or, interestingly enough, against those who refused to admit colonists from overpopulated countries to settle among them on lands that were being put to no profitable use. In the eyes of some, this last provision has made More the first advocate of British imperialism, but it is doubtful if he saw that far ahead.

It has been suggested that More wrote the *Utopia* in the hope of influencing Henry VIII. Handbooks for princes, written by those who wished to curry favor or who had genuinely at heart the good of the kingdom, were in vogue. Two years before the *Utopia* was published, Machiavelli, the gifted Florentine, had written *The Prince,* and dedicated it to Lorenzo di Medici. And only a few months before, Erasmus published *The Education of a Christian Prince,* a book prepared for the diffident Spanish youth who was soon to become Emperor Charles V. Erasmus may have had more reason for hoping that his teaching would take root, for Charles, in whose service he had just taken appointment, was only sixteen. Henry, too, was young; but there is a vast difference between sixteen and twenty-five (ask anyone who is twenty-five), and there is nothing to suggest that More cherished any hope that his advice would be taken seriously by his sovereign.

Henry was still his friend and well-wisher, but More seems to have sensed the fact that the young king had no disposition to listen to advice unless it accorded with his own wishes. Throughout Hythloday's analysis in Book I of the behavior of princes and of current international practices, there runs a note of pessimism. There has been no lack of good counsel written down for kings already, Hythloday says, first by Plato and then by others. But there has been no readiness on their part to take heed. They prefer to consider how they may—by fair means or foul—add to their dominions rather than "how well and peaceably to rule and govern them they have already." It is a convincing picture that he draws of what would happen if he sat down to the council table with the king of France and his other advisers, and More is forced to agree that the situation is pretty hopeless. Renaissance princes, one gathers, found Machiavelli's advice that "a prince who desires to maintain himself must learn to be not always good, but to be so or not as necessity may require," more to their liking than the high-minded principles of Erasmus and More.

Yet in the end More is not willing that the philosopher wash his hands of the job entirely just because he cannot accomplish all he wishes. "If you cannot . . . remedy vices which use and custom have confirmed, yet . . . you must not leave and forsake the commonwealth; you must not forsake the ship in a tempest." With skill and tact you must seek to handle the situation, "and that which you cannot turn to good, so order that it is not very bad."

It is this philosophy, one suspects, that kept More in the service of his king in the years that lay ahead. He was made a member of the King's Council in 1517. Other honors followed. Diplomatic missions have already been mentioned. He was appointed Under-Treasurer in 1521, and was also knighted in that year. Likewise in 1521 the King ordered Wolsey, then Chancellor, to take some of the younger men like More into his confidence in his work as mediator between Francis I and the Emperor. In 1523 More was chosen speaker of the House of

Commons. The next year he became High Steward of the University of Oxford, and in the following year, 1525, was awarded the same office at Cambridge. During the next three years he came continually into higher favor with his sovereign, and in 1529 he succeeded Wolsey as Lord Chancellor. But even this office, the highest the King had to bestow, could not compensate one of More's temperament for the sense of defeat that was often his, and for the irksome demands that such a life entailed. He no doubt enjoyed the challenge to his skill and ability, but often, as his letters show, he longed for the greener pastures where others browsed in the "sweet enjoyment" of literature and philosophy.

Not, however, until an issue emerged that in More's eyes involved an even greater loyalty than that which he owed his King, did he give up his service to the commonwealth. This was the conflict that arose after 1529 between himself and Henry over the latter's divorce from Catherine of Aragon and denial of the Pope's right to the headship of the Church of England. In reality it was but a part of the greater conflict between church and state that gave to the English Reformation its peculiar character. For along with economic and political upheavals, the age was destined also to undergo the great ecclesiastical and religious upheaval of the Reformation.

When More published the *Utopia* in 1516, Martin Luther was still a relatively unknown professor at Wittenberg, one of the smaller German universities. But in 1517 his Ninety-Five Theses, a declaration of faith and denunciation of abuse all rolled into one, were posted on the Castle Church door at Wittenberg.

And by 1520, Luther's ideas, further clarified and set forth in a series of famous pamphlets, became the basic tenets of the German Reformation. These pamphlets, imported into England almost as soon as they were printed, were sold by an Oxford bookseller. In 1521, Henry VIII, still a zealous son of the church, prepared his refutation. A presentation copy was bound in gold and sent by special messenger to Pope Leo X, who rewarded the author with the title, Defender of the Faith. It is ironical, but we have the story from both More and Roper that when More was consulted by the King about his work, he attempted to persuade Henry not to allow so much authority to the Pope. He pointed out that an earlier English law had considerably pared away the power of the papacy in England, and that if ever in the future there should be disagreement between them, Henry might find his present stand embarrassing. But the King turned a deaf ear to the philosopher.

Effort at reform of the church had, of course, begun much earlier. Forerunners to Luther can be found throughout the later Middle Ages; and humanist scholars of the North had now for some years been carrying on a crusade for religious and moral reforms of the highest order. Their criticism centered not on the church as an organization of the faithful, but chiefly on the practices and abuses within it. Of the great English humanists who were More's mentors in his early days, John Colet was his closest friend and the man who did most to turn him in the direction of reform. Colet had received his inspiration from Pico della Mirandola, an Italian humanist who sought to infuse into Christianity the idealistic teachings of Plato. This fusion of Christian faith with the pagan belief in reason and virtue was the essence of the Christian humanism of the time. It formed a basis for the religion that More gave to the Utopians, a kind of humanitarian deism which abhorred religious intolerance.

The influence of Erasmus on More was similar to that of Colet, and perhaps even greater. Religion was to him the peaceable "philosophy of Christ." Yet Erasmus could write with knife-like sharpness when denouncing existing evils. Colet too could address a meeting of clergy with a flow of invective that Luther might have envied. Their common zeal for reform led the humanists and Luther at first along the same path, but to More and Erasmus and their group, the unity of the faith and of Christendom under its apostolic head, the Pope, was fundamental to the preservation of Christianity itself. When it became clear that Luther's reform movement meant violence and disruption, their ways parted.

In his later activities against heresy and heretics, More appears to have gone against the principle of toleration practiced by the Utopians, though the question of his personal responsibility for the persecution that took place during his chancellorship is still a moot point. Certainly the charges of early pro-Protestant writers were exaggerated. An example is Froude's famous statement that as soon as More became chancellor, "the Smithfield fires recommenced." Actually, not until the last few months of More's term of office were any heretics burned at Smithfield, the great market place outside of London that served also as a place of execution. And there is no trustworthy evidence to show whether or not he was in any way responsible for the three burnings which took place there shortly before his resignation in 1531. As a layman he could not pass sentence on heretics. Only the bishop in the church court could do that. Any responsibility that More may have had in these cases rested on the possible issuance of writs for arrest and execution. In his own reply to the question regarding his position on heretics, he stated that it was "that vice of theirs and not their persons" that he attacked.[1]

But if words could kill, More would indeed have been a slayer of heretics; for in a stream of vituperative writing he threw the whole weight of his energies against the spread of the new doctrine. "The church must be one," he said, and he fought with all his might the losing battle to keep it so.

It is characteristic of the age of the Renaissance that much that was medieval persisted alongside the new, or that which was newly learned from antiquity. More's attitude toward the Reformation, both as early ally and later opponent, was distinctly in line with the medieval tradition. A critical approach towards religious questions had been a part of the spirit of inquiry that had grown increasingly among educated minds since the twelfth century. It had proved particularly well suited to English soil. Contact with the Italian humanists had stimulated this rationalistic approach and as we have seen, More and

[1] For discussion of this question, see A. F. Pollard, *Wolsey*, 1929, pp. 209-214; R. W. Chambers, *Thomas More*, 1935, pp. 274-282; E. M. G. Routh, *Sir Thomas More and His Friends*, 1934, pp. 188-199.

his friends identified themselves with it, in their effort for reform noted above.

There was another side of More rooted in a tradition that ran even deeper in the thought of the Middle Ages, namely, a belief that it was only through Christianity and a united church that there was any hope of gaining peace and harmony and the brotherhood of man in a troubled world. In his support of this doctrine, he showed the deep feeling and moral earnestness of the medieval preacher. Though far removed from St. Bernard in many ways, there was something of the monk of Clairvaux in More's feeling for the church. It is difficult to prove that he ever went against the right of the individual privately to believe as he wished. That was the rationalist in him. But the influence of an avowed disbeliever he feared and fought against *because it was disruptive.* In his eyes a break in the unity of Christendom would be the greatest calamity that could befall. He says quite clearly in the *Utopia* that the man who was exiled for his religious intolerance was punished not because he was a despiser of the religion of others, but "as a seditious person and an inciter of dissension among the people." It was in this spirit that he carried forward his fight against heresy.

There was also in More something of the medieval ascetic. While still a student he had been greatly attracted to the monastic life. For almost four years he had lived with the Charterhouse monks in London, not taking vows, but sharing their life as fully as his studies would permit. He debated with himself whether to enter the priesthood or continue with the law as his father wished him to do. The attractive young daughters of John Colt, an Essex squire, helped him make his decison. He married Jane, the eldest of them, about 1505. But years later, when a prisoner in the Tower, he confided to his daughter Margaret that he had never quite lost his longing for the cloister. Nor must it be forgotten that for a considerable period of his life he wore next to his body the haircloth shirt of the penitent. The medieval and modern met in Sir Thomas More, recently canonized as Saint Thomas More, as the past must ever merge itself with the new in any age.

The delight of the Renaissance scholars in learning has already been mentioned. Love of learning drew men of like temperament together. After his arrival in England in 1499, Erasmus confided to a friend that except for a certain curiosity that he had to see Italy, he had almost lost his desire to go there, "so abundant is the harvest of ancient learning to be had in England."[2] More was then only twenty-one, and Erasmus some ten years his senior, but the friendship that began almost with their first meeting lasted throughout life. "My own affection for the man," wrote Erasmus of More, "is so great that if he bade me dance a hornpipe I should do at once just as he bade me. . . . I do not think . . . that nature ever formed a mind more ready, sharp-sighted and subtle, or more furnished with every kind of faculty than his." And More spoke of Erasmus with equal affection. Erasmus' wit was sharper, and more satirical, More's just as subtle, but with a gay or merry turn. His sense of humor helped him through many a difficult situation. Gay bantering

[2] This and the following quotation are from *Epistles of Erasmus*, edited by F. M. Nichols, 1901, I, 17, 406.

proved the best method of handling a wife whose sharp tongue would have made her a trial to some husbands. An amusing story or jest often relieved the tension of a political debate or a strained moment in the court room. Nor was it a quality that failed him even at the end, for as he climbed the scaffold steps on that fateful Tuesday of St. Thomas Eve, Thomas More followed his own preachment set down years before in the *Utopia*, and went "merrily to meet death."

It was while a guest in the More home in 1509 that Erasmus wrote *The Praise of Folly*. He did not come as often after More's second marriage. Perhaps Dame Alice did not appreciate a guest who had no liking for English beer, wanted his salads mixed with oil and vinegar in the French manner, and never troubled to speak English. But he still came occasionally and by means of letters the two friends kept in close touch.

Though always lamenting the fact that his public and professional career left him no leisure for study and literary activity, More managed to find time to produce a sizable body of writing in both Latin and English which included works in history, biography, poetry, and theology. But it was the *Utopia* which secured for its author his permanent place in literature. This was due partly to its own freshness and originality, partly to the fact that More's plan for an ideal state became a popular pattern. From his time to our own, "Utopian" literature has flourished in almost every generation. Bacon's *New Atlantis*, Harrington's *Oceana*, Campanella's *City of the Sun*, William Morris' *News from Nowhere*, and Samuel Butler's *Erewhon*, are but a few of the more famous examples.

More also showed the versatility of his age in his nice mingling of the practical and theoretical. Early in his career as a lawyer, he had begun to think and act in terms of public service. In 1510, as Under-Sheriff in the city of London, he became legal adviser to the Mayor and the two Sheriffs and represented them as judge for the city. This brought him in touch with the public services. In 1514, he was appointed one of the Commissioners of Sewers for the left bank of the Thames, thus becoming aware of the need for city planning and of questions of public health and sanitation. The Utopians, it will be noted, controlled such matters by the most careful planning.

Except in the fields of literature and architecture, More's own countrymen were lamentably backward in the arts, where Italian names—and after them, French, Spanish, and Flemish—added such luster to the Renaissance. But what they could not create, the English encouraged; and one remembers More's part in bringing Hans Holbein, the younger, to England. His home was opened to the great Dutch artist as to other men of talent. It was partly More's influence that secured him an appointment as court painter. To Holbein we are indebted for our knowledge of the appearance of More and Erasmus, and his drawing of the members of the More household has given the readers of More and Roper a feeling akin to intimacy with that family group. It appears to have been made in 1529, the year that More was appointed to the Chancellorship. Holbein sent Erasmus a sketch of it and Erasmus wrote enthusiastically to Margaret Roper, More's eldest daughter: "Holbein's picture showed me your whole family almost as faithfully as if I had you before my eyes." [3]

This household brings to mind one further field of Renaissance activity, that of education, for most of the young people in the drawing were members of More's "school." One would expect an age that glorified learning to pay attention to the theory and practice of education. A glance at the writings of some of the chief Renaissance educators leaves us with the impression that our own ideas of "progressive" schooling are not so new, after all. True, one novel feature of their program was getting Greek into the school curriculum, whereas most of the innovators of our day seem bent on getting both Greek and Latin out. But much of it has a familiar ring. Education must be made attractive to the student; it must seek to develop the *whole* child, physical, moral, and intellectual. It is easy to see here the reflection of the Greek ideal of the fully rounded personality. John Colet was perhaps even better known as an educator than as a religious reformer. He founded St. Paul's, a school for boys in London, which became something of a practice school in which to try out new theories.

Less well known, but also revolutionary in its time, was More's educational experiment, which included training for women. When it became apparent that his three daughters, Margaret, Elizabeth, and Cecily, had good minds, More determined to give them the best education he could secure. There was also a son, John, and, in addition, More's love for young

[3] Reprinted in T. E. Bridgett, *Life and Writings of Sir Thomas More,* 1891, p. 150.

people led him to take several others into his family and to have them share in the education that he was providing for his own children.

While in the royal service More had to be away from home a good deal and the letters that he wrote to his children reveal much concerning their educational program. They studied Greek and Latin, logic, philosophy, natural history, theology, and astronomy. To assist in the teaching of natural history, More kept a collection of animals and birds about his house and garden. It was a good thing that his wife shared her husband's love for animals, or this laboratory technique would not have been possible. Dame Alice was not a scholar, but she was a good manager and to keep the wheels of this large household running smoothly was no mean task.

More's educational plan was obviously not designed for girls only, but the fact that it included girls was the feature which aroused most attention. Aware that his experiment was being watched, he wrote, "Since learning in women is a new thing, and a reproach to the slothfulness of men, many will be ready to attack it." [4] As he showed in the *Utopia,* he believed in the mental equality of the sexes. "The harvest," he wrote, "will not be affected whether it be a man or woman who sows the seed. Both are reasonable beings, distinguished in this from the beasts; both therefore are suited equally for those studies by which reason is cultivated." Erasmus, who was devoted to More's family

[4] This and the following quotations are from More's letter to William Gonell, in *Correspondence of Sir Thomas More,* edited by E. F. Rogers, 1947, pp. 121-122.

thought the "new example" in women's education had been so successful that others would surely imitate it.

It is More's environment as a man of the Renaissance and interests and pursuits carried forward in common with men of his stamp throughout Western Europe that have thus far received attention. But despite this broad quality of his mind and spirit, More was nonetheless a warmhearted Englishman, a fact revealed many times in the *Utopia*. One who knows the old London is aware at once what city it was that provided the geographical pattern for the Utopian capital, Amurote. And who but an Englishman would have divided the islands into fifty-four shires?

The second book of the *Utopia*, written while More was on the Continent, had described a country as it might be if all were well. The first book, in which the conditions in England were so fully discussed, was written after his return from abroad. He was back again at his law practice, which brought him in contact with life among the poor of London. His mind was on the woes of his own country, as well as on the wider problem of international relations, of which he had but recently been getting some experience. Readers of the *Utopia*, therefore, will do well to have a look also at More's England—the England of the early Tudors.

The Cornish uprising against increased taxation, by which More has Raphael Hythloday date his visit to England, had occurred in 1497. Curiously enough, this is the same year that another traveler, an Italian, came to England in the company of a group of Venetian diplomats. His name has been lost, but his account of the visit remains,[5] and it is interesting to compare some of his impressions with those which More put into the mouth of Hythloday.

It is obvious that the Italian was impressed with the nation's wealth. He had been told that England was the richest country in Europe and he was inclined to agree. "Everyone who makes a tour of the island will soon become aware of this wealth." He was excited over the window displays of the silversmiths in London and thought their equal could not be found in all the shops of Milan, Rome, Venice, and Florence put together. He observed that the riches of London belonged not only to the noblemen and gentlemen, but were shared by craftsmen and "persons of low degree," and that many apprentices rose to good fortunes. Our Venetian also traveled about the countryside, and although he noted the absence of large urban centers, a contrast to the situation in his own country, he was again impressed by the wealth and its spread into many hands. He gave as an example the small innkeeper who served his table with silver dishes and drinking cups. He remarked on the wealth of the religious endowments, both that of the enormously rich Benedictine, Carthusian, and Cistercian monasteries, "more like baronial palaces than religious houses," and also that of ordinary parish churches, with their beautiful crucifixes, candlesticks, and cups of silver.

He noticed certain defects. Like Hythloday, he saw there was much thievery, and he was curious over some of the judicial and

5 *A Relation of the island of England*, Camden Society Publications, London, 1847.

political practices. But in the main one gets from him a picture of a prosperous country, with the wealth spread well into the middle and lower ranks, and with opportunities for advancement from the lower to the upper levels of society.

His picture is too rosy in spots. Not every innkeeper in early Tudor England had silver dishes on his table; nor was every parish church or convent furnished with treasures "worthy of a cathedral." There were, however, many people in the lower classes on their way up. And if he had traveled into the region of the rural clothiers of Essex or westward through the Cotswold hills he would have found beautiful new stone farmhouses (still beautiful after four centuries of weathering), and magnificent parish churches, furnished as richly as his record states. For the cloth trade, which had suffered something of a slump in the early and mid-fifteenth century, had now entered upon a new era of prosperity. The grain-growing Midlands and the dairy farms of East Anglia would likewise have appeared prosperous. There is, in fact, no symbol of wealth in all his record that he may not have seen, possibly many times over.

What then of the darker colors that emerge in Hythloday's narrative? The answer is that they too were there. And one cannot have a correct picture without taking both sides into account. For the same conditions—that is, high prices, rise in living standards, the commercialization of agriculture, etc.—that brought opportunity to some brought dismal failure to others. Even within the same social and economic group individuals might be affected either adversely or favorably by the turn of fortune's wheel.

INTRODUCTION

More was city bred. His description of the conditions that prevailed in London is acute and penetrating. His legal practice too brought him in contact with all sides of London life, the prosperous as well as the seamy. Rich merchants were his clients, as well as thieves and beggars. Hence when he put into Hythloday's mouth a description of the administration or maladministration of English justice, and laid bare the methods employed in dealing with crime and punishment, he knew exactly what he was talking about. In like manner, his acquaintance with the lower strata of the London population enabled him to speak with first-hand knowledge and authority of men driven by unemployment to hunger, by hunger to crime, and by crime into the arms of the law.

When, however, he turned from these conditions to their causes and attributed society's ills, even the high prices, chiefly to greedy landlords who were all growing rich at the expense of their poor tenants, he was merely accepting without qualification the picture of rural society that was the stock in trade of the preachers and pamphleteers of his day, men more to be commended for their humanitarian impulses than for their accuracy. A whole body of popular literature, mostly writings of a socio-religious nature, had grown up on this theme, the pattern of which was pretty much as More gives it. The land was full of thieves, "sturdy beggars" and "idle vagabonds" whose plight was caused partly by their own improvidence in following the "newfangledness" in styles of living, but chiefly they were the victims of misfortune not of their own making. They were servingmen cast off because their masters had no further use for them, or cloth workers, or farm tenants who had been forced off their land by cruel landlords ruthlessly enclosing tilled fields for sheep pasture, or demanding higher rents than the tenants were able to pay. By one method or another the tenant was being evicted, often from land his family had worked for generations. The inclosure of farm lands for pasture had driven all prices up, and the high prices in turn led to suffering, want, and often eventually to crime.

That the rise in prices, which was to continue on an even greater scale in the years to come, was the greatest single cause of the current hardship and suffering, is probably true. But to attribute all high prices to the inclosures was as fallacious as it was common. The price revolution, as the historians label this phenomenon, was, as we have seen, taking place all over Western Europe as a result of the interplay of numerous economic forces.

It was equally a mistake to assume that all inclosures were bad, or that they were the work of the landlords alone. Much inclosing was done not from crop lands but from forest, waste, and fen, which, rather than decreasing opportunities of habitation and employment, reclaimed hundreds of acres that became for the first time habitable and productive. Inclosure, moreover, increased the value of the land. Some contemporaries held that an acre of inclosed land was worth an acre and a half of uninclosed; some put the rates much higher. So the tenants themselves, who were as eager to improve the productivity of their land as were their lords, often either initiated inclosures or were themselves willing partners in the venture. There are many accounts of such action taken by common agreement, "for the general good and benefit of the whole town and all the inhabitants."

There were cases of conversion to pasturage which produced real hardship and these might well have increased had not social critics like More and his fellows agitated for government action against them. One act to restrict inclosures was passed in 1489, another in 1515, the year before the *Utopia* was published. But a vast amount of careful study by modern economic historians has led to the conclusion that the lands reclaimed for settlement by inclosure offered opportunities for habitation which more than compensated for the sporadic "depopulation" that occurred. Since ejection by inclosure when it did happen was particularly obnoxious, it was often held responsible "for ills not its own progeny."

A second part of More's picture needing qualification is his assumption that the landlord was always the villain in the piece. This popular misconception probably grew out of the fact that the rise in prices often affected different members of the same class quite unevenly. It could happen that some tenants on a given manor, selling their corn and sheep for high prices, were accumulating capital and prospering in a way unknown to their forefathers, while others of the same status in the same locality, possibly even on the same manor, were being forced to pay rents or renewal fines that eventually drove them out of their lands entirely. Prices of farm produce had soared along with other prices, making agriculture a highly profitable enterprise. Hence it was to be expected that both rents and fines would rise accordingly. But whether they actually did or not depended much on the nature of the tenure, or terms on which the tenant held his land.

The cost of living for the gentry and nobility was also rising. As an expanding commerce and industry brought more varied and richer articles within their reach, standards of taste and comfort became more exacting. And since many desirable things must be brought in from outside markets, the prices demanded for them were high. Silk bedhangings, even if the wife and daughters did the needlework, were expensive. So were silver plate, Venetian glassware, "printed cloths" or tapestries, joined furniture, and the like. Yet inventories attached to wills indicate that these were the things that the Tudor gentry had in their houses; and gentlemen must live up to their station. Travel was also more expensive for the son who wished to visit Italy; and it cost more to maintain him at Oxford or Cambridge or as a law student at one of the Inns of Court. A daughter who married must be provided with a larger dowry, and the high cost of food made the dispensing of hospitality—so necessary a function of the gentry—more expensive.

Caught thus, the knights and gentlemen, eager at least to maintain themselves in the station to which they belonged, sought ways and means to make their incomes exceed or at any rate balance their outgo. They might raise the fines and rents of their tenants at the expiration of their terms of tenure. If the old tenant could meet the new demands, well and good. If not, there were other applicants for his place who would gladly pay the increased rent and the increased fine in order to get the land they wanted. The landlord might decide that he would get the best returns from his land by leasing it for relatively short terms at a high cash price. Tenants ejected by these methods fell into the class of landless laborers. They might maintain themselves for a time at piece work or day labor. They might even get on their feet again as tenants of another landlord or find good paying jobs in nearby towns. But labor was plentiful once again in England, as it had not been throughout a good part of the fifteenth century, and evicted farmers might be forced into the ranks of the unemployed, often the prelude to vagrancy and beggardom.

This was the course that matters could and often did take, and had there been no other, More and the other social critics would have been right in making the tenant the perennial victim of the landlord. But it might happen that the landlord's manor was one on which the land was *freehold*. Freeholders had permanent rights of tenure. They were, moreover, free from most of the manorial obligations, except perhaps attendance at court, or the payment of a small nominal rent, or a red rose or a pound of pepper at Christmas time. Or it might be the special kind of *copyhold* land that passed regularly from father to son, as did freehold, for which the fines and rents were "fixed and certain," and had been so time out of mind. These lands offered the tenant practically the same security as did freehold. In either of these cases the landlord's hands were tied: he could neither eject the tenant nor raise rents or fines.

Unable, therefore, to keep his own expenses down, but barred from raising his income by increased rents, the landlord might be forced to sell off parts of his estate. Often the *demesne,* as the lord's own land was called, was sold piece by piece to thrifty tenants. Or the whole might be sold outright to a wealthy merchant or draper or vintner, who had made a fortune in trade and now desired to set up as a country gentleman. Certain it was that one man's loss was another's gain. Many were successful, but success could not be taken for granted. It was a period of growing competition, and one who was not industrious, ambitious, and thrifty, or one who could not save enough during fat years to tide him over the lean ones, might not weather the storm. This combined opportunity and danger made the situation something of a gamble. It put a premium on individual initiative and aggressiveness; riches increasingly became the measure of achievement. It was this spirit of competition and materialism that More deplored as much as he grieved over the suffering of those who fell victim to it.

More was not alone in his concern for the social ills of his time. A growing number of his contemporaries raised their voices in protest against a society in which the rich seemed to grow richer and the poor to sink into greater poverty. Indeed, from *Piers Plowman* on, England had had her champions of the poor who railed against greed and avarice and pride as the greatest evils of humankind, and along with their protest preached a kind of Christian democracy. Mostly such critics defended the social structure of the day, but not always. Old John Ball, a century before More, had been three times clapped into Maidstone jail for airing his views too boldly. But he continued to stop people on their way home from church to remind them that all was not well with England, or ever would be, until equality had been attained and "the lords be no greater masters than we be." So when More put into Hythloday's mouth the bitter indictment of the social wrongs of England, he was speaking wholly within the medieval tradition. But his work is distinguished from that of both his predecessors and his conporaries by its approach to the solution of the problem; in fact, by his belief that there can be a solution. His firmness also in fixing social responsibility places him ahead of his own age and abreast of the enlightened social thinkers of later generations.

The remedy prescribed by most medieval preachers for the evils which they attacked was simply to love God with greater devotion, and hate the devil fiercely enough to avoid getting caught in his snares. To the first dictum More subscribed heartily; but one way of loving God more fully, he suggests, is through the mind as well as the heart. This the Utopians had learned, "that reason chiefly and principally kindles in men the love and veneration of Divine majesty." Again it is the Christian humanist in More coming to the fore.

In respect to the ills of society, moreover, Hythloday is made to say that it is not the fault of the individual that he is led to crime, but of circumstances beyond his control. Society has not the right to allow youth to grow up in an environment of idleness and vice and then punish them by death for crimes that are merely acts on a larger scale of what they have done all their lives: "I pray you what other thing do you do than make thieves and then punish them?" In the nineteenth century England at last heeded More's plea for penal reform, but his insistence that the punishment be made to fit the crime is an ideal not yet anywhere wholly attained.

One after another Hythloday takes up conditions that make for misery, poverty, unhappiness, and crime. He then goes on to show by argument and by illustrations from Utopia that unemployment and poverty are not inevitable, that they are subject to improvement and cure if men as rational beings set themselves to the task; and that such matters are the proper concern, indeed the imperative obligation, of society. This is More's greatest contribution to the literature of social thought, and on it rests his just claim to rank as a pioneer.

The years of active law practice brought More in touch not only with unemployment and poverty but with other human problems. Had he been intent only on a successful professional career, these matters would have been to him only a part of the day's work; but in his spare time he conversed with friends on the nature of the good life, and read Plato and Aristotle to see how they thought it could be attained. They had pondered many of the same problems that confronted him and he mingled their ideas with his own experience. He saw that there had always been much wrong with life as men lived it together. If one could really create a society in which people acted rationally and in accord with the best ideals of pagan and Christian, what would it be like?

More's answer to that question was the *Utopia,* the name coined from the Greek meaning "nowhere"—land of nowhere, but land of might-be. The place where lawyers are not needed because laws are few and simple enough to be understood by all;

where no one is idle and the fruits of labor are shared equally; where a short working day leaves leisure for everyone to take pleasure in living; where wealth is not measured in terms of gold and silver but in things of the mind and spirit. In Utopia, moreover, the vexed problems of human relationships are handled with intelligence and understanding. Marriage bonds are held sacred, but sometimes divorce is recognized as just and wise. The older generation and the young get along without friction and are happy together, honoring each other. The very ill are cared for in beautifully appointed hospitals, but if perchance incurable disease makes life a burden, one need not live on; for suicide under such circumstances merits no disapproval. In Utopia there are churches where beautiful music, lighted candles, and the odor of burning incense create an atmosphere suited to the spirit of worship. But if that is not what one likes in religion, it will not be forced upon him. In Utopia neighbor helps neighbor, and nation—almost always—helps nation. States that are knit together by love and kindness are considered better off than those joined by covenants that are likely to be broken. These and many more principles characterized life in Utopia. Some of them have long since been in practice among us; some are as revolutionary to the twentieth century as they were to the sixteenth.

To what extent More himself believed practicable all of the ideas and customs that he attributed to the Utopians, or would have been willing to attempt to put them into effect in his own age, is a debatable question—and probably will be as long as his book is read. From his day to our own there have been those who believed that the *Utopia* was merely a delightful fantasy, written for the entertainment of Renaissance intellectuals and to be enjoyed as one would enjoy any piece of first-rate imaginative literature. Others have considered it a revolutionary document that provides a blue-print for radical and social political action. And still others hold that it is the work of a social philosopher, who, like the Socratic gadfly, regarded it his duty to startle men's minds and provoke them to thought on problems that have a right to their attention. Earlier generations concerned themselves most with the Utopians' religious views; in our day it is their practice of communism that evokes the greatest interest and divergence of opinion.

Frankly acknowledging his debt to the *Republic* of Plato, More has Hythloday declare that many of the gravest social ills would be removed if only men held their possessions in common, thus doing away with the motive of private gain. Hythloday speaks out plainly on the subject: "Thus do I fully persuade myself that no equal and just distribution of things can be made, nor perfect wealth ever be among men, unless their proprietorship be exiled and banished." Later More replies in his own person. "But I am of a contrary opinion . . . for methinks that men shall never live wealthily there, where all things are held in common. For how can there be abundance of goods, or of anything, where every man holds back his hand from labor? Where regard for his own gains drives not to work."

The question is whether Hythloday is here speaking for More, as he seems to do elsewhere, or whether More is speaking for himself. Marxists have held the former view. They con-

sider More one of the first great Socialists and contend that only
in modern times with the rise of Marxian socialism has it become possible fully to understand the significance of his work.[6]
Anti-Marxists, in an effort to show that Hythloday was not
expressing More's real sentiments, quote from his other writings on the same subject: "Men of substance must there be, for
else you shall have more beggars. . . . If all the money that is
in this country were tomorrow brought together out of every
man's hand, and laid upon one heap and then equally divided
among all, it would be on the morrow after worse than it was
the day before . . . for the best should be left little better
then than almost a beggar is now. . . . Surely the rich man's
substance is the wellspring of the poor man's living." [7]

Other readers, possibly more detached, have felt that More
himself was greatly taken with the theory of communism and
thought of it as an ideal system, but believed also that there
could be such an ideal commonwealth only if there were ideal
men with whom to people it. This is explicitly stated: "For it is
not possible for all things to be well unless all men are good.
Which I think will not be yet these good many years." And
these interpreters quote the last paragraph in the *Utopia*, which
seems designed, whether by conscious intent of the author or
not, to leave the dogmatist of whatever persuasion forever in
the lurch: "In the meantime, as I cannot agree and consent to all
things that he [Hythloday] said, being else without doubt a man
singularly well learned, and in all worldly matters exactly and

[6] Kautsky, *Thomas More and His Utopia*, 1927.
[7] *A Dialogue of Comfort*, Everyman's Library, Book II, pp. 254-255.

profoundly experienced, so must I needs confess and grant that there are many things in the Utopian commonwealth which in our cities I may rather wish than hope for."

Still others look upon More not as the protagonist of a particular doctrine, but as one deeply sensitive to human suffering, whose interpretation of the Christian ideal included a strong sense of social obligation and a rational attitude of mind, willing to grapple with new ideas. Communism was one of the new ideas that presented itself. Like a true son of the Renaissance he offered it as a challenge that would at least stimulate men's thinking and thereby open the way to social progress. Studies of More's theories will continue to be made; men will debate the meaning of the *Utopia,* and discuss the author's position on this or that question. They will continue to create ideal worlds of their own to show humanity how much better life might be if only men would work to make it so. In so doing they will focus attention on fundamental questions, fundamental in More's day and in ours. It is, one suspects, a role for the *Utopia* with which its author would be well content.

MILDRED CAMPBELL

THE *UTOPIA*

The traditional arrangement of the *Utopia* presented here does not follow the order in which it was written; for the second book was written first, probably in 1515 at Antwerp. In the following year, home again from abroad, More wrote the part that was to appear in print as Book I. It provides a framework for Book II, and serves somewhat as an introduction to it. More's letter to Peter Giles, a friend in Antwerp, and Giles' letter to Jerome Busleiden, as well as the Verses and the note from the Printer to the Reader, are printed here in the order in which they appeared in the first edition. They are all a part of the mechanism designed to lend reality to the tale. Devices of this kind, partly borrowed from the classics, were much in favor among the humanists, who with obvious enjoyment went to great pains to endow their works of imagination with all the earmarks of reality.

Under the direction of Erasmus and the same Peter Giles who wrote the letter, the first edition of the *Utopia,* in the original Latin, came from the press in Louvain in 1516. A second edition appeared in Paris in 1517, another in Basle the following year, and in 1519 there were editions published in Florence, Vienna, and Venice, eloquent testimony to the popularity of the work. Soon translations were in demand, and oddly enough, there were translations in French, Italian, and Dutch before the first English one, that of Ralph Robinson, reached the public in 1551.

UTOPIA

The present text, modernized with respect to spelling, archaic words, and an occasional change in sentence structure made in the interest of clarity, remains essentially the translation of Ralph Robinson, which even in semi-modern dress contains more of the spirit and character of More's own day than can possibly be achieved in a modern translation.

Thomas More to Peter Giles[1]
sends greeting

𝕴 AM ALMOST ashamed, right well-beloved Peter Giles, to send to you this book of the Utopian commonwealth after well-nigh a year's space, which I am sure you looked for within a month and a half. And no marvel! For you knew well enough that in this work I was not burdened by any of the labor and study that belong to invention, and that I had no need at all to trouble my brains about the disposition or arrangement of the material, and therefore had nothing else to do with it but only repeat the things which you and I together heard Master Raphael tell and declare.[2] So there was no reason why I should endeavor to set forth the material with eloquence, since his talk could not be fine and eloquent, being, in the first place, not studied but spontaneous and unpremeditated, and besides, as you know, the talk of a man better versed in the Greek language than in the Latin tongue. And the nearer my writing should approach to his homely, plain, and simple speech, so much the nearer would it come to the truth, which is the only aim toward which I do and should direct all my toil and study herein.

[1] On Peter Giles of Antwerp, see the information given in the *Utopia*, p. 16.
[2] On Raphael Hythloday and his meeting with More and Giles, see p. 17.

I grant and confess, friend Peter, that I was relieved of much labor, having all these things ready done to my hands, so that there was almost nothing left for me to do. Otherwise either the invention or the disposition of the material would have required of a mind, neither base nor altogether unlearned, both time and leisure and also some study. And if it had been requisite and necessary that the book should also be written with eloquence and not merely with truth, that certainly I could not have done with any time or study. But now since all the cares, hindrances, and obstructions were absent, on which otherwise so much labor and effort would have been spent, and there remained nothing else for me to do but only to write plainly the story as I heard it told, that was indeed a slight thing and easy to be done.

Howbeit for the dispatch of this little business, my other cares and troubles left me almost less than no leisure. One while, I am every day putting my time on law matters—on some as pleader, on some as hearer, on some as an arbitrator with my award to determine, on some as an umpire or a judge with my sentence finally to declare. Another while, I am going one way to see and visit my friends, another way about my own private affairs. At times I spend almost all day abroad with others, the rest at home with my own. I leave no time for myself, I mean for my book. For when I come home, I must converse with my wife, chat with my children, and talk with my servants. All of which I reckon and count as business, since it must of necessity be done; and done it must needs be, unless a man would be a stranger in his own house. And in some way a man must so fashion and order his circumstances and so govern and deport

himself as to be merry, jocund, and pleasant with those whom
either nature has provided, or chance has made, or he himself
has chosen to be the companions of his life; yet so too as not to
spoil them with too much easy behavior and familiarity, and not,
by too much tolerance toward his servants, make them his
masters. Amid these things now described, steal away the day,
the month, the year.

When then do I write? All the while I have said no word of
sleep, nor yet of eating, on which a great number waste no less
time than they do on sleep, wherein almost half the lifetime of a
man creeps away. I then win and get only that time which I
steal from sleep and eating. Which time is very little and yet is
something, and therefore have I now at last, though it is a long
first, finished *Utopia,* and have sent it to you, friend Peter, to
read and peruse, with the intent that if anything has escaped me,
you might put me in remembrance of it.

For though on this matter, I do not greatly distrust myself—
would God I were something in wit and learning, as in memory
I am not at all the worst and dullest—still I have not such great
trust and confidence in it that I think nothing could fall out of
my mind. For John Clement, my boy, who, as you know, was
present there with us, and whom I keep with me at every talk
in which there may be profit or goodness (for from this young
blade and newly shot up corn, which has already begun to
spring up in both Latin and Greek learning, I look for plentiful
increase, in time, of goodly, ripe grain), he, I say, has raised in
me a great doubt. For whereas Hythloday, unless my memory
fail me, said that the bridge at Amaurote, which crosses the

river Anyder, is five hundred paces, that is to say, half a mile in length, my John says that two hundred of those paces must be stripped off, because the river there is not over three hundred paces in breadth. I pray you with all my heart to recall the matter to your remembrance. For if you agree with him, I too will say what you say and confess myself mistaken. But if you cannot surely remember the thing, then I will write as I have done and as my own memory serves me. For as I will pay good heed to have in my book nothing false, so if there is anything doubtful, I would rather tell a lie than make a lie, because I would rather be good than crafty.

Howbeit, this matter may easily be settled if you will take the pains to ask the question of Raphael himself, by word of mouth, if he is now with you, or else in your letters. This you must needs do for another doubt that has arisen, through whose fault I cannot tell—whether through mine or yours or Raphael's. For neither did we remember to inquire of him nor he to tell us in what part of the new world Utopia is situated. I had rather have spent a great sum of money than to have this knowledge escape us, both because I am ashamed to be ignorant of the sea in which that island lies on which I have written so long a treatise, and also because there are with us certain men, and especially one virtuous and godly man, a professor of divinity, who is exceedingly desirous of going to Utopia, not for a vain and inquisitive desire to see novelties but with the intent that he may further and spread our religion, which has there already happily been started.

And in order the better to accomplish and carry out his good purpose, he is minded to procure that he be sent thither by the high Bishop; yea, and that he himself be made Bishop of Utopia, for he is not scrupulous over the point that he must obtain this bishopric by suit. For he counts it a goodly suit that is conducted not out of desire for honor or lucre but only for godly zeal.

Wherefore I most earnestly desire you, friend Peter, to talk with Hythloday, face to face, if you can, or else to write letters to him and so to labor in this matter that in this my book there neither be found anything which is untrue nor anything lacking which is true. And I verily think it will be well if you show him the book itself. For if I have missed or failed at any point, or if any fault has escaped me, no man can so well correct and amend it as he can; and that he cannot do without perusing and reading over my book as written. Moreover, by this way you will perceive whether he is quite willing and content that I should undertake to put this work into writing. For if he is minded to publish and report his own labors and travels himself, perchance he may be loath, and so would I be also, that by publishing an account of the Utopian commonwealth, I should anticipate him and take from him the flower and grace of novelty of this his story.

Howbeit, to speak the very truth, I am not yet fully decided myself whether I will publish my book or not. For the natures of men are so diverse, the fancies of some so wayward, their minds so unkind, their judgments so corrupt that they think those who lead a merry, gay life, following their own sensual pleasures and carnal lusts, are in much better state and condition than those who vex and trouble themselves with cares and efforts to put out and publish something that may be a profit or pleasure to some, but which others nevertheless will take disdainfully, scornfully, and unkindly. The greater part of all people are unlearned, and a large number hold learning in contempt. The rude and barbarous man likes nothing but what is truly barbarous indeed.

If there is one who has a little smack of learning, he rejects as homely stuff and common ware whatever is not stuffed full of old, moth-eaten phrases, that are worn past use. Some there are who find pleasure only in old, rusty antiquities, and some only in their own doings. One is so sour, so crabbed, and so unpleasant that he can tolerate no mirth or sport. Another is so narrow between the shoulders that he can bear no jests or taunts. Some silly, poor souls are so afraid that at every snappish word their nose shall be bitten off that they stand in no less dread of every quick and sharp word than a man bitten by a mad dog fears water. Some are so changeable and wavering that every hour they have a new mind, and say one thing sitting and another thing standing. Another sort sit on their court benches and there amid their cups issue judgments on the wits of writers and with great authority condemn as they please every writer according to his writing, mocking, louting, and flouting them in the most spiteful manner, while they themselves meanwhile sit safe and, as the proverb says, out of all danger of gunshot. Why, they are so smug and smooth that they have not so much as a hair of an honest man, by which one might take hold of them! There are likewise some so unkind and ungenerous that though they take great pleasure and delight in a word, still for all that they cannot find it in their hearts to love the author thereof or to spare him a good word. For they are much like discourteous, unthankful, and churlish guests, who when they have filled their stomachs well with good and dainty meats, depart home, giving no thanks to the feast-maker. Go your ways now and make a costly feast at your own charge for guests so dainty mouthed, so diverse in taste and, besides that, so unkind and unthankful in nature!

But nevertheless, friend Peter, do, I pray you, consult with Hythloday, as I asked you before. And for this matter, I shall be at liberty afterwards to consider it afresh. Howbeit, seeing that I have taken great pains and labor in writing of the matter, if it accord with his mind and pleasure, I will, as regards the editing and translating of the book, follow the counsel and advice of my friends, and especially yours. Thus fare you well right heartily, beloved friend Peter, with your gentle wife; and love me as you have ever done, for I love you better than ever I did.

A Fruitful and Pleasant Work of the Best State of a Public Weal and of the New Ile Called Utopia: Written in Latin by Sir Thomas More, Knight, and Translated into English by Ralph Robinson, Citizen and Goldsmith of London.

*The First Book of the Conversation of Raphael
Hythloday concerning the best state of a
Commonwealth.*

THE MOST victorious and triumphant King of England,
Henry the Eighth of that name, in all royal virtues, prince
most peerless, had of late, in controversy with the right high and
mighty King of Castile, weighty matters and of great importance, for the debatement and final determination whereof, the
King's Majesty sent me ambassador into Flanders, joined in
commission with Cuthbert Tunstall, a man beyond compare,
and whom the King's Majesty of late, to the great rejoicing of
all men, did appoint to the office of Master of the Rolls.

But of this man's praises I will say nothing, not because I
fear that small credence shall be given to the testimony that
comes out of a friend's mouth, but because his virtue and learning are greater, and of more excellence than I am able to praise,
and also in all places so famous and so perfectly well known
that they need not nor ought not of me to be praised, unless I
would seem to show and set forth the brightness of the sun
with a candle, as the proverb says.

There met us at Bruges (for this it was before agreed) they
whom their Prince had for this matter appointed commissioners

excellent men all. The chief and the head of them was the Margrave, as they call him, of Bruges, a right honorable man; but the wisest and best spoken of them was George Temsice, provost of Cassel, a man not only by learning but also by nature of singular excellence, and in the laws profoundly learned; but in reasoning and debating of matters, what by his natural wit and what by daily exercise, surely he had few equals. After we had once or twice met, and upon certain points or articles could not fully and thoroughly agree, they for a certain space took their leave of us, and departed to Brussels, there to know their Prince's pleasure. I in the meantime (for so my business lay) went straight thence to Antwerp.

While I was there I was oftentimes among the others, but my most welcome visitor was one Peter Giles, a citizen of Antwerp, a man of honest reputation there in his country, and also appointed to high offices, worthy truly of the highest. For it is hard to say whether the young man be in learning or in honesty more excellent. For he is both of a wonderfully virtuous behavior, and also singularly well learned, and towards all sorts of people exceeding gentle; but towards his friends so kind-hearted, so loving, so faithful, so trusty, and of such earnest affection, that it would be very hard in any place to find a man who with him in all points of friendship may be compared. No man can be more lowly or courteous. No man uses less pretense, in no man is more prudent simplicity. Besides this, he is in his talk and conversation so merry and pleasant, yea and that without harm, that through his gentle entertainment, and his sweet and delectable conversation, there was in me greatly abated and diminished the fervent desire that I had to see my native country, my wife, and my children, whom then I did much long and covet to see, because at that time I had been more than four months from them.

Upon a certain day when I had heard the divine service in our Lady's church,[1] which is the fairest, the most gorgeous and curious church building in all the city and also most frequented of people, and, the service being done, was ready to go home to my lodging, I chanced to espy this foresaid Peter talking with a certain stranger, a man well stricken in age, with a black sunburned face, a long beard, and a cloak cast carelessly about his shoulders, whom by his face and apparel forthwith I judged to be a mariner. But when this Peter saw me, he comes to me and salutes me.

And as I was about to answer him, "See you this man," says he, and therewith he pointed to the man that I saw him talking with before; "I was minded," quoth he, "to bring him straight home to you."

"He should have been very welcome to me," said I, "for your sake."

"Nay," quoth he, "for his own sake, if you knew him: for

---

[1] The cathedral of Notre Dame in Antwerp is the finest piece of Gothic architecture in Belgium and one of the best specimens in Western Europe. Some of the Renaissance work was added after More's visit, but much of the best work was already completed. One of the windows that he would view with interest was the gift of Henry VII and his Yorkist bride Elizabeth, in commemoration of Henry's treaty with Philip I of Castile in 1506. The combined red and white rose form a feature of its ornamentation.

Fortunately, the bombings of World War II did no damage to "our Lady's church" at Antwerp.

there is no man this day living that can tell you of so many strange and unknown peoples and countries as this man can. And I know well that you are very desirous to hear of such news."

"Then I conjectured not far amiss," quoth I, "for even at the first sight I judged him to be a mariner."

"Nay," quoth he, "there you were greatly deceived: he has sailed indeed, not as the mariner Palinure,[2] but as the expert and prudent prince Ulysses; yea, rather as the ancient and sage philosopher Plato. For this same Raphael Hythloday (for this is his name) is very well learned in the Latin tongue, but profound and excellent in the Greek tongue, whereon he ever bestowed more study than on the Latin, because he had given himself wholly to the study of philosophy. Whereof he knew that there is nothing extant in the Latin tongue that is to any purpose, saving a few of Seneca's and Cicero's doings. His patrimony that he was born unto, he left to his brethren (for he is Portuguese born) and because of the desire that he had to see and know the far countries of the world, he joined himself in company with Amerigo Vespucci, and in the three last voyages of those four that are now in print and abroad in every man's hands,[3] he continued still in his company, saving that in the last voyage he came not home again with him. For he

[2] Palinurus, the helmsman of Aeneas, as related in the *Aeneid* of Vergil, went to sleep at his post, and fell off into the sea.

[3] The work referred to is the *Four Voyages of Amerigo Vespucci*, first published in 1507. In his account of the fourth voyage (1503), Vespucci speaks of a garrison of twenty-four men who were left behind on the coast of Brazil. It is obvious that this incident furnished More with a scaffolding for his story.

made such means and shift, what by entreaty, and what by importunate suit, that he got license of master Amerigo (though it were sore against his will) to be one of the twenty-four which in the end of the last voyage were left in the country of Gulike. He was therefore left behind to gratify his whim as one that took more thought and care for traveling than dying, having customarily in his mouth these sayings: 'He that hath no grave is covered with the sky'; and, 'The way to heaven out of all places is of like length and distance.' For which fantasy of his (if God had not been his better friend) he had surely paid full dear. But after the departing of Master Vespucci, when he had traveled through and about many countries with five of his Gulikian companions, at the last by marvelous chance he arrived in Taprobane,[4] from whence he went to Calicut, where he chanced to find certain of his country's ships, wherein he returned again into his country, to everyone's surprise."

When Peter had told me all this, I thanked him for his gentle kindness that he had vouchsafed to bring me to speak with this man, whose conversation he thought should be to me pleasant and acceptable. And therewith I turned me to Raphael. And

---

The account Vespucci gives of his second voyage ade in 1501 is also significant, as he relates in it his visit to a strange people living in an unidentified part of "those regions," who held all of their possessions in common and displayed a number of other traits later attributed by More to his Utopians. Historians have discredited much that was contained in Vespucci's accounts, but they fired the imaginations of the sixteenth century, as did the tales of other voyagers, and More did well to play upon this interest.

[4] A word that grew out of the corrupted Greek form of the native name for Ceylon.

when we had saluted each other, and had spoken the common words that are customarily spoken at the first meeting and acquaintance of strangers, we went thence to my house, and there in my garden upon a bench covered with green turf we sat down talking together. There he told us how, after the departing of Vespucci, he and his fellows, that tarried behind in Gulike, began little by little, through fair and gentle speech, to win the love and favor of the people of that country, insomuch that within short space they did not only dwell amongst them harmless, but also traded with them very familiarly. He told us also that they were in high reputation and favor with a certain great man (whose name and country is now quite out of my remembrance) who of his mere liberality did bear the costs and charges of him and his five companions; and besides that, gave them a trusty guide to conduct them in their journeying, which by water was in boats and by land in wagons, and to bring them to other princes, with very friendly commendations.

Thus after many days' journeys, he said, they found towns and cities and states full of people, governed by good and wholesome laws. "For," quoth he, "under the equinoctial line, and on both sides of the same, as far as the sun extends his course, lie great and wide deserts and wildernesses, parched, burned, and dried up with continual and intolerable heat. All things are hideous, terrible, loathsome, and unpleasant to behold; all things uncouth and without comeliness, inhabited by wild beasts and serpents, or at the least, by people that are no less savage, wild, and harmful than the very beasts themselves. But a little farther beyond that, all things begin little by little to wax pleasant; the air soft, temperate, and gentle; the ground covered with green grass; less wildness in the beasts. At the last you shall come again to people, cities, and towns wherein is continual intercourse and traffic in merchandise, not only among themselves and with their neighboring peoples, but also with merchants of far countries, both by land and water.

"There I had opportunity," said he, "to go to many countries on every side. For there was no ship ready for any voyage or journey, but I and my fellows were very gladly received into it." The ships that they found first were made plain, flat, and broad in the bottom, trough-wise. The sails were made of great rushes, or of wicker, and in some places, of leather. Afterwards they found ships with ridged keels, and sails of canvas, yea, and shortly after, others having all things like ours. The shipmen also were very expert and cunning, both in the sea and in the weather. But he said that he found great favor and friendship among them, for teaching them how to use the loadstone,[5] which to them before that time was unknown. And therefore they were wont to be very timorous and fearful upon the sea, nor to venture upon it, but only in the summer time. But now they have such confidence in that stone that they fear not stormy winter; and hence are freer from worry than from peril, inso-

[5] Both the Chinese and the Arabs are credited with the invention and use of the magnetic compass. Knowledge of it came to Christian Europe in the twelfth century from Spain, though a thirteenth century treatise declared that no master mariner dared make use of it, lest he be suspected of practicing magic. It does not appear to have been used as a practical aid to navigation until the fifteenth century.

much that it is greatly to be doubted lest that thing, through their own foolish hardiness, may turn out to do them evil and harm, which at the first was supposed to be to them convenient and good.

But what he told us that he saw in every country where he came, would be very long to declare; neither is it my purpose at this time to make rehearsal thereof. But peradventure in another place I will speak of it, chiefly such things as shall be profitable to be known, as in special are those decrees and ordinances that he noted were well and wisely provided and enacted among such peoples as live together in a civil polity and good order. For of such things did we busily inquire and demand of him, and he likewise very willingly told us of the same. But as for monsters, because they are no news, we were not inquisitive of them. For nothing is more easy to be found than barking Scyllas, ravening Celenos, and Laestrygonian devourers of people, and such-like great and incredible monsters.[6] But to find citizens ruled by good and wholesome laws, that is an exceeding rare and hard thing. But as he remarked upon many poor and foolish laws in those new-found lands, so he related many acts and constitutions, wherefrom our cities, nations, countries, and kingdoms may take example to amend their faults, enormities, and errors, whereof in another place (as I said) I will treat.

Now at this time I am determined to relate only what he told us of the manners, customs, laws, and ordinances of the

[6] These are the monsters Ulysses and Aeneas met in their wanderings, as described in Homer's *Odyssey* and Vergil's *Aeneid*.

Utopians. But first I will repeat our former conversation, by the occasion and (as I might say) the drift whereof, he was brought to mention that commonwealth.

For Raphael very prudently touched on divers things that are amiss, some here and some there, yea, very many in both regions; and again spoke of the wise and prudent laws and decrees that are established and used, both here among us and also there among them, as a man so cunning and expert in the laws and customs of every country, as if into what place soever he came as guest, there he had lived all his life; then Peter, much marveling at the man, "Surely, Master Raphael," quoth he, "I wonder greatly why you go not to some king's court. For I am sure there is no prince living that would not be very glad to have you, as a man not only able highly to delight him with your profound learning and your knowledge of countries and peoples, but also fitted to instruct him with examples, and help him with counsel. And thus doing, you shall raise yourself to a very good state, and also be enabled to help all your friends and kinsfolk."

"As concerning my friends and kinsfolk," quoth he, "I have no great regard for them. For I think I have sufficiently done my part towards them already. For the things that other men part not from until they are old and sick, yea, which they then are very loath to leave when they can no longer keep them, those very same things did I, when not only lusty and in good health but even in the flower of my youth, divide among my friends and kinsfolk. This my liberality I think ought to hold them contented, not to demand or expect that besides this J should for their sakes give myself in bondage to kings."

"Nay, God forbid!" quoth Peter. "It is not my mind that you should be in bondage to kings, but a retainer to them at your pleasure; which surely, I think, is the best way you can devise how to bestow your time fruitfully, not only for the private advantage of your friends and for the general profit of all sorts of people, but also for the advancement of yourself to a much wealthier state and condition than you are now in."

"To a wealthier condition," quoth Raphael, "by means to which my mind stands clean against? Now I live at liberty after my own mind and pleasure, which I think very few of these great statesmen and peers of realms can say. Yea and there are enough of them that seek for great men's friendships: and therefore think it no great hurt if they have not me, nor two or three others such as I am."

"Well, I perceive plainly, friend Raphael," quoth I, "that you are desirous neither of riches nor of power. And truly I hold in no less reverence and estimation a man that is of your mind than any of them all that are so high in power and authority. But you shall do as becomes you: yea, and according to this wisdom and this high and free courage of yours, if you can find in your heart so to engage and dispose yourself that you may apply your wit and diligence to profit of the public good, though it be somewhat to your own pain and hindrance. Yet this you shall never so well do, nor with so great profit perform, if you are not of some great prince's council, and put into his head (as I doubt not but you will) honest opinions and virtuous persuasions. For from the prince, as from a perpetual wellspring, comes among the people the flood of all that is good or evil. But so perfect is your learning and so great your experience that on the strength of either you might well be any king's councilor."

"You are twice deceived, Master More," quoth he, "first in me, and again in the thing itself. For neither is that ability in me that you force upon me, nor if it were should I in disturbing my own tranquillity further the public good. For first of all, the majority of princes have more delight in warlike matters and feats of chivalry, the knowledge whereof I neither have nor desire, than in good feats of peace; and spend much more study on how by right or by wrong to enlarge their dominions than on how well and peaceably to rule and govern what they have already. Moreover, they that are councilors to kings, every one of them, either is of himself so wise indeed that he need not, or else thinks himself so wise that he will not accept another man's counsel, save that they do shamefully and flatteringly assent to the silly and foolish sayings of certain great men; whose favors, because they are in high authority with their prince, by assent and flattery they labor to obtain. And verily it is naturally given to all men to esteem their own inventions best. So both the raven and the ape think their own young ones fairest. Then if a man in a company where some disdain and have contempt for other men's discoveries and count their own best, if among such men, I say, a man should bring forth anything that he has read was done in times past, or that he has seen done in other places, then the hearers act

as though their whole reputation for wisdom were in jeopardy
of being overthrown, and that ever after they would be counted
for very fools, unless they could in other men's ideas pick out
matter to reprehend and find fault at. If all other poor helps
fail, then this is their extreme refuge. 'These things,' say they,
'pleased our forefathers and ancestors; would God we could
be so wise as they were.' And as though they had wittily concluded the matter, and with this answer stopped every man's
mouth, they sit down again. As if they would say, it were a
very dangerous matter, if a man in any point should be found
wiser than his forefathers were.

"And yet we are content to suffer the best and wisest of their
decrees to lie unexecuted: but if in anything a better order
might have been set up than was by them, there we take fast
hold, and find many faults. Many times have I chanced upon
such proud, ignorant, perverse, and wayward judgments; yea,
and once in England."

"I pray you, sir," quoth I, "have you been in our country?"

"Yea, forsooth," quoth he, "and there I tarried for the space
of four or five months together, not long after the insurrection
that the western Englishmen made against their king,[7] which
by their own miserable and pitiful slaughter was suppressed
and ended. During my stay I was much bound and beholden
to the right reverend father, John Morton, Archbishop and

[7] The uprising of 1497 in which Cornishmen under Lord Audley's spirited leader-
ship marched all the way to London to show their indignation against a tax
levied for carrying on the Scottish wars. They were defeated on Blackheath
Common by troops of King Henry VII.

Cardinal of Canterbury,[8] and at that time also Lord Chancellor of England: a man, Master Peter (for Master More knows already what I will say), not more honorable for his authority than for his prudence and virtue. He was of medium stature, and though stricken in age, yet he bore his body upright. In his face did shine such an amiable reverence as was pleasant to behold, gentle in talk, yet earnest and sage. He took great delight many times in rough speech to his suitors, to prove, though without harm, what prompt wit and what bold spirit were in every man; in which, as in a virtue much agreeing with his nature, so long as impudence was not therewith joined he took great delectation. And the same person, as apt and well suited to have an office in the commonwealth, he would lovingly accept. In his speech he was fine, eloquent, and pithy. In the law he had profound knowledge, in wit he was incomparable, and in memory wonderfully excellent. These qualities, which in him were by nature singular, he by learning and use had made perfect. The king put much trust in his counsel. The commonwealth also in a manner leaned upon him, when I was there. For even in the flower of his youth he was taken from school into the court, and there passed all his time in much trouble and business, and was continually tumbled and tossed in the waves and divers misfortunes and adversities. And so by many and great dangers he learned experience of the world, which so being learned can not easily be forgotten.

[8] Cardinal Morton, minister of Henry VII, was one of the last great churchmen to hold office in the royal administration in England. See Roper's *Life of More,* p. 210.

"It chanced on a certain day, when I sat at his table, there was a certain layman learned in the laws of your realm, who taking some occasion, I know not what, began diligently and busily to praise that strait and rigorous justice which at that time was there executed upon poor wretches, who, as he said, were for the most part twenty hanged together upon one gallows.[9] And, seeing so few escaped punishment, he said he could not choose, but greatly wonder and marvel, how and by what evil luck it should so come to pass that thieves nevertheless were in every place so plentiful. 'Nay, sir,' quoth I, for I durst boldly speak my mind before the Cardinal, 'marvel nothing hereat, for this punishment of thieves passes the limits of justice, and is also very hurtful to the commonwealth. For it is too extreme and cruel a punishment for theft, and yet not sufficient to restrain men from theft. For simple theft is not so great an offense that it ought to be punished with death. Neither is there any punishment so horrible that it can keep men from stealing who have no other craft whereby to get their living. Therefore in this point, not you only, but also the most part of the world, are like evil schoolmasters, readier to beat than to teach their scholars. For great and horrible punishments are appointed for thieves, whereas much rather, provision should have been made to provide some means whereby they might get their living, so that no man should be driven

[9] Others besides More raised their voices against the use of capital punishment for theft. It remained for years a favorite theme of the social critics; but it was not until the reform of the penal code in 1827 that the practice became illegal in England.

to this extreme necessity, first to steal, and then to die.'
"'Yes,' quoth he, 'this matter is well enough provided for
already. There are handicrafts, there is husbandry to get their
living by, if they would not willingly remain in such poor
condition.' 'Nay,' quoth I, 'you shall not 'scape so. I will first
of all say nothing of those that come home out of war, maimed
and lame, as not long ago, out of Blackheath field, and a little
before then, out of the wars in France; such, I say, as put
their lives in jeopardy for the commonwealth or the King's
sake, and by reason of weakness or lameness are not able to
work at their old crafts, and are too aged to learn new. Of
them I will say nothing, because war like the tide ebbs and
flows. But let us consider those things that chance daily before
our eyes. First there is a great number of gentlemen who cannot be content to live idle themselves, like drones, on that which
others have labored for: their tenants, I mean, whom they shave
and cut to the quick by raising their rents (for this one kind
of frugality do they practice, men who else through their lavish
and prodigal spending may bring themselves to very beggary).
These gentlemen, I say, not only live in idleness themselves,
but also carry about with them at their tails a great flock or
train of idle and loitering servingmen, who never learned any
craft whereby to get their livings.[10] These men, as soon as their

[10] This picture of the sad state of things in England appears again and again
in the popular literature of the sixteenth century, particularly the early half
of the century. It follows pretty much the same pattern, with greedy landlords,
spendthrift gentlemen, idle servingmen, and impoverished tenants as the chief
figures in the scene; and depopulation, crime, poverty, excessive punishments,
and increasing vagabondage its characteristic features. But the preachers and

master is dead, or they are sick themselves, are forthwith thrust out of doors. For gentlemen had rather keep idle persons than sick men; and many times the dead man's heir is not able to maintain so great a house, and keep so many servingmen as his father did. Then they who for the time being are thus out of service, either starve for hunger, or manfully play thieves. For what would you have them do?

" 'When they have wandered abroad so long that they have worn threadbare their apparel and also impaired their health, then gentlemen, because of their pale and sick faces and patched coats, will not take them into service. And farmers dare not set them at work, knowing well enough that he is all unfit to do true and faithful service to a poor man with a spade and mattock for small wages and hard fare, who was daintily and tenderly pampered up in idleness and pleasure, and was wont with a sword and buckler by his side to strut through the street with a bragging look, and think himself too good to be any man's mate.' 'Nay, by Saint Mary, sir,' quoth the lawyer, 'not so. For this kind of men we must make most of. For in them, as men of stouter stomachs, bolder spirits, and manlier courage than handicraftsmen and plowmen, consists the whole power, strength, and puissance of our army, when we must fight in battle.'

" 'Forsooth, sir, as well might you say,' quoth I, 'that for war's sake you must cherish thieves, while you have this kind.

---

pamphleteers, chief among those who delivered ceaseless invective, were too often aware of the symptoms only and possessed little understanding of the complex economic and social forces that worked to produce them.

No, thieves are not the most false and faint-hearted soldiers, and soldiers are not the cowardliest thieves, as well as these two crafts agree together. But this fault, though it be prevalent among you, yet is not peculiar to you only, but common also to almost all nations. And France, besides this, is troubled and infected with a much sorer plague. The whole realm is filled and beset with hired soldiers in peace time (if that be peace), who are brought in under some color and pretense that has persuaded you to keep these idle servingmen. For those wise fools and very archdolts thought the wealth of the whole country to consist in this: that there should be ever in readiness a strong and a sure garrison, especially of old practiced soldiers, for they put no trust at all in men untrained. And therefore they must be fain to seek for war, to the end they may ever have practiced soldiers and cunning manslayers, lest—as it is prettily said by Sallust, their hands and their minds through idleness or lack of exercise should wax dull. But how pernicious and pestilent a thing it is to maintain such beasts, the Frenchmen, to their own injury, have learned, and the examples of the Romans, Carthaginians, Syrians, and many other countries do manifestly declare. For not only the empire, but also the fields and cities of all these, on divers occasions have been overrun and destroyed by their own armies held beforehand in readiness. Now how unnecessary a thing this is, hereby may appear: the French soldiers, who from their youth have been practiced and inured in feats of arms, do not brag or boast themselves to have very often got the upper hand and mastery of your new-made and unpracticed soldiers. But on this point

I will not use many words, lest perchance I may seem to flatter you. No, and those same handicraftsmen of yours in cities, and the rude and uplandish plowmen of the country, are not supposed to be greatly afraid of your gentlemen's idle servingmen, unless there be some of body and stature unequal to their strength and courage, or whose bold stomachs are discouraged through poverty. Thus you may see that it is not to be feared lest the others should be made effeminate, if they were brought up in good crafts and laborsome works, whereby to get their living. Those stout and sturdy bodies (for gentlemen vouchsafe to corrupt and spoil none but picked and chosen men) are now either by reason of rest and idleness brought to weakness, or else by too easy and womanly exercises made feeble and unable to endure hardness.

" 'Truly, however the case stands, this methinks is nothing profitable to the public weal; for war's sake, which you never have, save when you yourselves will to keep and maintain an innumerable flock of that sort of men that are so troublesome and annoying in peace, whereof you ought to have a thousand times more regard than of war.

" 'But yet this is not the only necessary cause of stealing. There is another, which, as I suppose, is proper and peculiar to you Englishmen alone.' 'What is that?' quoth the Cardinal. 'Forsooth,' quoth I, 'your sheep, that were wont to be so meek and tame, and such small eaters, now, as I hear say, are become such great devourers and so wild that they eat up and swallow down the very men themselves. They consume, destroy, and devour whole fields, houses, and cities. For look in what parts of the realm grows the finest and therefore dearest wool, there noblemen and gentlemen, yea and certain abbots, holy men, God wot, not content with the yearly revenues and profits that were wont to flow to their forefathers and predecessors on their lands, nor content that they live in rest and pleasure while nothing profiting, yea much annoying, the public weal, leave no ground for tillage, but enclose all in pastures. They throw down houses; they pluck down towns, and leave nothing standing, but only the church, to make of it a sheep-house.[11] And as though you were not losing great quantity of ground in forests, chases, lawns, and parks, those good holy men turn all dwelling places and all glebe-land into desolation and wilderness.

" 'Therefore, because one covetous and insatiable cormorant and plague of his native country may compass about and inclose many thousand acres of ground together within one fence or hedge, the husbandmen are thrust out of their own, or else by cunning and fraud, or by violent oppression are deprived of it, or by wrongs and injuries are so wearied that they are compelled to sell it all. By one means, therefore, or another, either by hook or by crook, they must needs depart, poor, silly, wretched souls, men, women, husbands, wives, fatherless children, widows, woeful mothers, with their young babes, and their whole households, small in substance and much

---

[11] Enclosures of fields and other cultivated land for use as sheep pasture provided one of the chief objects for complaint among the social critics of the day. But it is wrong to assume, as many writers have done, that contemporary opinion was wholly against the practice. See Introduction.

in number, as farming requires many hands. Away they trudge, I say, out of their known and accustomed houses, finding no place to rest in. All their household stuff, which would be worth little, even though it were allowed to await a good buyer, yet being suddenly thrust out, they are constrained to sell it for a trifle. And when, wandering about, they have soon spent that, what can they do but steal, and then justly, God wot, be hanged, or else go about a-begging. And then they are cast in prison as vagabonds, because they go about and work not: whom no man will set at work, though they willingly offer themselves thereto. For one shepherd or herdsman is enough to eat up that ground with his cattle, for the tilling of which in farming many hands were requisite. And this is also the cause that victuals are now in many places dearer. Yea, besides this, the price of wool is so risen that poor folks, who were wont to work it and make cloth of it, are now able to buy none at all. And by this means many are fain to forsake work and give themselves to idleness.

" 'For after so much ground was enclosed for pasture, an infinite multitude of sheep died of the rot. Such vengeance God took of their inordinate and insatiable covetousness, sending among the sheep that pestiferous murrain,[12] which much more justly should have fallen on the sheepmasters' own heads. And

12 A general term used to include various virulent diseases that attacked domesticated animals. "The plague" was another term used with the same meaning. There was little knowledge for either its prevention or cure, and whole flocks of sheep were often swept away in a single season with no further explanation among those who had lost by it than that offered above, that it was an act of God.

though the number of sheep increase never so fast, yet the price falls not one bit, because there are so few sellers. For they almost all come into a few rich men's hands, whom no need drives to sell before they wish, and they wish not until they may sell as dear as they desire. Now the same cause brings in like dearth of the other kinds of cattle, and that so much the more, because after farms are pulled down and farming decayed, there is no man that cares for the breeding of young stock. For these rich men bring not up the young of great cattle as they do lambs, but first they buy them abroad very cheap and afterward, when they are fatted in their pastures, they sell them again exceeding dear. And therefore, as I suppose, the whole inconvenience hereof is not yet felt. For as yet they create high prices only in those places where they sell. But when they shall fetch them away from places where they are bred faster than they can be raised, then there too shall be felt the increased cost, when the supply begins to fail, where the ware is bought.

" 'Thus the unreasonable covetousness of a few has turned that thing to the utter undoing of your island, in which the chief felicity of your realm did consist. For this great dearness of victuals causes every man to keep as few houses and as small hospitality as he possibly may, and to put away his servants; whither, I pray you, but a-begging, or else (which these gentle bloods and stout stomachs will sooner set their minds to)—a-stealing? Now surpassing even this, to this wretched beggary and miserable poverty is joined great wantonness, grievous extravagance, and excessive riot. For not only gentlemen's servants, but also handicraftsmen, yea and almost the plowmen of the country, with all sorts of other people, use much strange and proud newfangleness in their apparel, and much prodigal riot and sumptuous fare at their table. Now bawds, loose women, whores, harlots, strumpets, brothel-houses, stews, wine-taverns, ale houses and tippling houses, with so many naughty, lewd, and unlawful games, as dice, cards, tables, tennis, bowls, quoits, —do not all these send the haunters of them straight a-stealing when their money is gone?

"'Cast out these pernicious abominations, make a law that they who pulled down farms and farmsteads shall build them up again, or else yield and render up the possession of them to such as will go to the cost of building them anew. Suffer not these rich men to buy up all, to engross and forestall [13] and with their monopoly to keep the market alone as pleased them. Let not so many be brought up in idleness, let farming and tillage be restored again, let clothworking be renewed, that there may be honest labors for these idle people to pass their time in profitably, whom hitherto either poverty has caused to be thieves, or else are now either vagabonds, or idle servingmen, and shortly will be thieves. Doubtless, unless you find a remedy for these enormities, you shall in vain pride yourself on executing justice upon felons. For this justice has more the appearance than the actuality of justice. For you suffer your youth to be wantonly and viciously brought up, and infected, even from their tender

[13] Laws designed to control the markets were passed as early as the reign of Henry III, and periodically after that time. "Engrossing" referred to the practice of hoarding grain during cheap years until the prices should be better. "Forestalling" was the buying or contracting for produce before it reached the market.

age, little by little, with vice, then in God's name to be punished after they come to man's state, when they commit the same faults which from their youth they were ever used to do. On this point, I pray you, what other thing do you do but make thieves and then punish them?'

"Now as I was thus speaking, the lawyer began to make himself ready to answer, and was determined to use the common fashion and manner of disputers, who are more diligent in relating than in answering, as if thinking that memory deserves the chief praise.

" 'Indeed, sir,' quoth he, 'you have spoken well, being but a stranger and one who would rather hear something of these matters than have any exact or perfect knowledge of the same, as I will immediately by open proof make manifest and plain. For first I will repeat in order all that you have said; then I will declare in what way you are deceived, through lack of knowledge, in all our fashions, manners, and customs; and last of all, I will answer your arguments and confute them every one. First, therefore, I will begin where I promised. Four things, you seemed to me——'

" 'Hold your peace,' quoth the Cardinal, 'for you will make no short answer who make such a beginning. Wherefore at this time you shall not take the pains to make your answer, but keep it for your next meeting, which I would be right glad that it be tomorrow, unless either you or Master Raphael know any serious hindrance. But now, Master Raphael, I would very gladly hear of you, why you think theft not worthy to be punished with death, or what other punishment you can devise more expedient to the public good. For I am sure you are not of that mind that you would have theft escape unpunished. For if now the extreme punishment of death cannot cause them to stop stealing, then if ruffians and robbers were sure of their lives, what violence, what fear would be able to keep their hands from robbing, who would take the mitigation of the punishment as a very provocation to the mischief?'

" 'Surely, my lord,' quoth I, 'I think it not right nor just that the loss of money should cause the loss of a man's life. For my opinion is that all the goods in the world are not the equivalent of a man's life. But if they would say that the violation of order and the transgression of the laws are requited with this punishment, and not the loss of the money, then why may not this extreme justice well be called extreme injustice? For neither so cruel governance, so stern rules, and unmerciful laws are allowable that for one small offense committed, at once the sword should be drawn; nor such harsh ordinances to be borne withal, as to count all offenses so nearly equal that the killing of a man or the taking of his money from him, are both an offense, and the one no more heinous than the other; between which two, if we have any respect for equity, no similitude or equality exists. God commands us that we shall not kill. And are we then so hasty to kill a man for taking a little money? And if any man would understand killing by this commandment of God to be forbidden no further than as man's constitutions define where killing is lawful, then why may it not likewise be determined by man's constitutions after what sort whoredom, fornication. and perjury may be lawful? For whereas, by ordinance of God.

no man has power to kill either himself or yet any other man, then if a law made by consent of men concerning the slaughter of men should be of such strength, force, and virtue, that they who, contrary to the commandment of God, have killed those whom the constitution of man commanded to be killed are clean quit and exempt from the bonds and jurisdiction of God's commandment, shall it not then by this reason follow that the power of God's commandment extends no further than man's law defines and permits? And so it shall come to pass that in like manner man's constitutions in all things shall determine how far his observance of all God's commandments shall extend.

" 'To be brief, Moses' law, though it was ungentle and sharp, as a law that was given to bondmen—yea, and them very obstinate, stubborn, and stiff-necked—yet it punished theft through the purse, and not with death. And let us not think that God in the new law of clemency and mercy, under which he rules us with fatherly gentleness as his dear children, has given us greater scope and license to execute cruelty, one upon another.

" 'Now you have heard the reasons whereby I am persuaded that this punishment is unlawful. Furthermore, I think there is nobody that does not know how unreasonable, yea, how pernicious a thing it is to the public weal that a thief and a homicide or murderer should suffer equal and like punishment. For the thief, seeing that a man who is condemned for theft is in no less jeopardy, nor judged to no less a punishment than he who is convicted of manslaughter, through this thought only he is strongly and forcibly provoked, and in a manner constrained to kill him whom else he would have but robbed. For the murder once done, he is in less fear, and in more hope that the deed shall not be betrayed or known, seeing the party is now dead and rid out of the way, who alone might have uttered and disclosed it. But if he chance to be discovered and taken, yet he is in no more jeopardy than if he had committed a mere theft. Therefore, while we go about with such cruelty to make thieves afraid, we provoke them to kill good men. Now as touching the question what punishment would be more suitable and better: that truly, in my judgment, is easier to be found than what punishment would be worse. For why should we doubt that a good and profitable way for the punishment of offenders, which we know did in times past so long satisfy the Romans, men most expert, politic, and cunning in the administration of a common-wealth? Such as among them were convicted of great and heinous trespasses, them they condemned to stone quarries and mines to dig metal, and there to be kept in chains all the days of their life.

" 'But regarding this matter, I approve the ordinance of no nation so much as what I saw while I traveled abroad about the world, practiced in Persia among the people that commonly are called Polylerites,[14] whose land is both large and ample, and

[14] The *Polylerites* had their origin in Thomas More's imagination, as did various other peoples whose names appear on the succeeding pages, the *Achorians*, the *Macariens*, the *Nephelogetes* and the *Alaopolitanes*, and the *Zapoletes*. It will be observed that all of these terms stem from the Greek, and most of them like the term *Utopia* itself (a combination of two words meaning *No-where*), appear to have been devised with some intent as to their meaning, *e.g. Polylerites*, meaning *Much nonsense*. Scholars of More have busied themselves with interpretations of these, but some of them defy exact interpretation. In cases like the above where

also well and wisely governed, and whose people in all conditions free and ruled by their own laws, save that they pay a
yearly tribute to the great king of Persia. But because they are
far from the sea, compassed and closed in almost round about
with high mountains, and do content themselves with the fruits
of their own land, which is of itself very fertile and fruitful,
they neither go to other countries, nor others come to them. And
according to the old custom of the land, they desire not to
enlarge the bounds of their dominions; and those that they have,
by reason of the high hills, are easily defended; and the tribute
which they pay to their chief lord and king sets them quiet and
free from warfare. Thus their life is comfortable rather than
showy, and may better be called happy or lucky than notable or
famous. For they are not known even by name, I suppose, save
only to their next neighbors.

" 'They that in this land are attainted and convicted of felony
make restitution of what they stole to the right owner, and not,
as they do in other lands, to the king, whom they think has no
more right to the thief-stolen thing than the thief himself. But
if the thing be lost or destroyed, then the value of it is paid with
the goods of the offenders, which else remains all whole to their
wives and children. And they themselves are condemned to be
common laborers, and, unless the theft is very heinous, they
are neither locked in prison nor kept in fetters, but are untied
and go at large, laboring on the public works. They that refuse
labor, or go slowly or slackly to their work, are more often

---

the meaning seems fairly obvious, it is of interest rather as an example of More's
whimsey than for any significance it may bear.

whipped than imprisoned. They that are diligent about their work live without check or rebuke. Every night they are called in by name, and locked in their chambers. Besides their daily labor, their life is nothing hard or uncomfortable. Their fare is moderately good, charged to the expense of the public, because they are common servants to the commonwealth. But their expense in all places of the land is not borne alike. For in some parts what is bestowed upon them is gathered as alms, and though that way is uncertain, yet the people are so full of mercy and pity that no other is found more profitable or plentiful. In some places certain lands are appointed thereto, by the revenues whereof they are maintained. And in some places every man pays a certain tax for the same use and purpose. Again in some parts of the land these servingmen (for so are these condemned persons called) do no public work, but as every private man needs laborers, so he comes into the market place, and there hires some of them for meat and drink, and a certain limited wage by the day, somewhat cheaper than he should hire a free man. It is also lawful for them to chastise the sloth of these servingmen with stripes. By this means they never are without work, and besides their meat and drink, every one of them brings daily something into the common treasury.

" 'All and every one of them are clothed in the same color. Their heads are not cropped or shaven, but rounded a little above the ears. And the tip of one ear is cut off. Every one of them may take meat and drink from their friends, and also a coat of their own color, but to receive money is death, as well to the giver as to the receiver. And no less peril is it for a free man 'o receive money from a servingman for any manner of cause, and likewise for servingmen to touch weapons. The servingmen of every shire are distinct and known from others by their several distinct badges, which to cast away is death, as it is also to be seen out of the precincts of their own shire, or to talk with a servingman of another shire. And it is no less danger to them to plan to run away than to do it indeed. Yea, and to conceal such an enterprise is death for a servingman; for a free man, servitude. On the other hand, to him that discloses and makes known such a plan are decreed large gifts; to a free man a great sum of money, to a servingman freedom, and to them both forgiveness and pardon for being involved in the intrigue. So that it can never be as good for them to go forward in their evil purpose, as by repentance to turn back. This is the law and order on this point, as I have showed you. Wherein what humanity is used, how far it is from cruelty, and how beneficial it is, you do plainly perceive; forasmuch as the end of their wrath and punishment is for nothing else but the destruction of vices and the saving of men, with so treating and ordering them that they cannot choose but be good, and what harm soever they earlier did, in the residue of their life to make amends for the same.

" 'Moreover, there is so little fear that they will turn again to their vicious conditions that travelers will for their safeguard choose them for guides before any other, in every shire changing and taking new. For if they wished to commit robbery, they have nothing about them suited to that purpose. They may touch no weapons; money found about them would betray the robbery. They would no sooner be caught in the act but forthwith they would be punished. Neither can they have any hope at all to escape by fleeing. For how should a man, that in no part of his apparel is like other men, flee secretly and unknown, unless he run away naked? Howbeit even so, as fleeing he would be detected by his rounding and his ear-mark. But is it to be feared that they will lay their heads together and conspire against the public weal? No, no, I warrant you. For the servingmen of one shire alone could never hope to bring to pass such an enterprise, without soliciting, enticing, and alluring the servingmen of many other shires to take part—which thing is to them impossible, since they may not as much as speak or talk together, or salute one another. No, it is not to be thought that they would take their own countrymen and companions into their counsel in such a matter which they know well would be in peril to the concealer thereof, and great advantage and goodness to the revealer of the same. While on the other hand, there is none of them all so hopeless or in such despair of recovering again his freedom that he will not by humble obedience, by patient suffering, and by giving good tokens and account of himself, ever after live like a true and an honest man. For every year some are restored again to their freedom, through the recommendation of their patience.'

"When I had thus spoken, saying moreover that I could see no cause why this order might not be set up in England with much more profit than the justice which the lawyer so highly praised: 'Nay,' quoth the lawyer, 'this could never be so established in England, but that it must needs bring the public weal into great danger and hazard.' And as he was thus saying, he shook his head, and made a wry mouth, and so held his peace. And all that were there present with one accord agreed to his saying.

" 'Well,' quoth the Cardinal, 'yet it is hard to judge without a proof whether this order would do well here or no. But when a sentence of death is given, if the king should then command execution to be deferred and stayed, and would test this order and method, taking away the privileges of all sanctuaries; [15] if the proof would show the thing to be good and profitable, then it were well it were established; if not, the condemned and reprieved persons could as well and as justly be put to death after this test, as at the outset. Neither can any jeopardy in the meantime arise hereof. Yes, and methinks these vagabonds may very well be treated after the same fashion, against whom we have made so many laws, and to so little avail.'

"When the Cardinal had thus said, then every man gave great praise to my words, which a little before they had disapproved. But most of all, they admired what was said of vagabonds, because it was the Cardinal's own addition. I cannot tell whether it were best to relate the conversation that followed, for it was not very serious. But yet you shall hear it, for there was no evil in it, and in part it pertained to the matter aforesaid.

[15] The right of a criminal to flee for refuge to consecrated soil, usually a church or church yard, was a recognized principle of criminal law throughout the Middle Ages. Abuses led to protests at least as early as the fourteenth century, and laws modifying the privilege were passed under Henry VIII. This legislation was repealed, but public opinion continued to grow against the practice, and rights of sanctuary were abolished in the early seventeenth century.

"There chanced to stand by a certain jesting parasite, or scoffer, who wished to act and counterfeit the fool. But he did
counterfeit so well that he was almost the very thing indeed
that he labored to imitate: he so studied with words and sayings
brought forth out of time and place to make sport and stir up
laughter that he himself was oftener laughed at than his jests
were. Yet the foolish fellow brought out now and then such
moderate and reasonable stuff that he made the proverb true,
which says: 'He that shoots oft shall at the last hit the mark.' So
that when one of the company said that through my conversation a good method was found for handling thieves, and that
the Cardinal also had well provided for vagabonds, so it only
remained to make some good provision for those who through
sickness and age were fallen into poverty, and were become so
impotent and infirm that they were not able to work for their
living. 'Tush,' quoth he. 'Let me alone with them. For I had
rather than anything that this kind of people were driven some-
where out of my sight; they have so sore troubled me many
times and oft, when they have with their lamentable tears
begged money of me, and yet they could never so tune their
song to my mind that they ever thereby got of me one farthing.
For evermore one of these two chanced: either I would not, or
else I could not, because I had it not. Therefore now they are
waxed wise. When they see me go by, because they will not
waste their labor, they let me go and say not one word to me.
So they look for nothing of me, no, in good sooth no more than
if I were a priest. But I will make a law that all these beggars
shall be distributed and bestowed into houses of religion. The

...nen shall be made lay brethren, as they call them, and the women nuns.'

"Hereat the Cardinal smiled, and took it in jest, yea and all the residue in good earnest. But a certain friar, graduate in divinity, took such pleasure and delight in this jest of priests and monks that he also, being at other times a man of grisly and stern gravity, began merrily and wantonly to jest and taunt. 'Nay,' quoth he, 'you shall not so be rid and despatched of beggars unless you make some provision also for us friars.' 'Why,' quoth the jester, 'that is done already, for my lord himself made a very good rule for you when he decreed that vagabonds should be kept confined and set to work, for you are the greatest and veriest vagabonds that are.'

"This jest also, when they saw the Cardinal did not disapprove it, every man took gladly, saving only the friar. For he (and that was no marvel), when he was thus touched on the quick and hit on the gall, so fretted, so fumed and chafed at it, and was in such a rage, that he could not refrain from chiding, scolding, railing, and reviling. He called the fellow 'ribald, villain, backbiter, slanderer, and the son of perdition,' citing therewith terrible threats out of Holy Scripture.

"Then the jesting scoffer began to play the scoffer indeed, and verily he was good at it, for he could play the part in that play, no man better. 'Compose yourself, good master friar,' quoth he, 'and be not angry, for Scripture says in your patience you shall save your souls.' Then the friar (for I will repeat his very words)—'No, gallows wretch, I am not angry, or at the least, I do not sin, for the Psalmist said, Be you angry and sin not.'

"Then the Cardinal spoke gently to the friar, and desired him to quiet himself. 'No, my lord,' quoth he, 'I speak not but out of good zeal as I ought: for holy men had a good zeal. Wherefore it is said: The zeal of the house has eaten me. And it is sung in the church that the scorners of Elisha, while he went up into the house to God, felt the zeal of the bald, as peradventure this scorning ribald villain shall feel it.'

" 'You do it,' quoth the Cardinal, 'perchance out of good will and affection; but methinks you would do perhaps more holily, certainly more wisely, if you would not match your wit with a fool's wit, and with a fool take hand in a foolish contention.' 'No, forsooth, my lord,' quoth he, 'I should not do more wisely. For Solomon the wise said, Answer a fool according to his foolishness, as I do now, and show him the pit he shall fall into, if he take not heed. For if many scorners of Elisha, who was but one bald man, felt the zeal of the bald, how much more shall one scorner of many friars feel, among whom are many bald men? And when we have also the pope's bulls, whereby all that mock and scorn us are excommunicated, suspended, and accursed.' [16]

"The Cardinal, seeing that no end would be made, sent away the jester by a private nod, and turned the conversation to

[16] The reference is to the familiar Biblical story of Elisha (2nd Kings II:23). The "scorners" were the forty-two children who cried "bald-head" at the prophet and were forthwith torn by she-bears. In the original Latin, More effects a misuse of words on the part of the friar in order to show up his lack of scholarship. It is, of course, to the shaved heads of the friars that the final references to "the bald" are made. The proverb quoted from Solomon is found in Proverbs, XXVI:5.

another matter. Shortly after, when he was risen from the table, he went to hear his suitors, and so dismissed us.

"Look, Master More, with how long and tedious a tale I have kept you, which surely I would have been ashamed to do, but that you so earnestly desired me, and did so closely give ear unto it, as though you would not have any part of that conversation left out. Which though I have done somewhat briefly, yet could I not choose but relate it, for judgment of them, who after they had disapproved and condemned my sayings, immediately upon hearing the Cardinal sanction them, did themselves also approve the same; flattering him so impudently that they were not ashamed to take, yea almost in good earnest, his jester's foolish inventions: because he himself by smiling at them did seem not to disapprove them. So by this you may right well perceive how little the courtiers would regard and esteem me and my sayings."

"I assure you, Master Raphael," quoth I, "I took great delight in hearing you; all things that you said were spoken so wittily and so pleasantly. And methought myself to be meanwhile, not only at home in my country, but also, through the pleasant remembrance of the Cardinal, in whose house I was brought up as a child, becoming a child again. And, friend Raphael, though I did bear very great love towards you before, yet as I see you so earnestly admire this man, you will not believe how much my love towards you is now increased. But yet, all this notwithstanding, I can by no means change my mind, but must needs believe that you, if you are so disposed, and can find in your heart to attend some prince's court, shall with your good

49

counsels greatly help and further the commonwealth. Wherefore there is nothing belongs more to your duty, that is to say, to the duty of a good man. For whereas your Plato judges that commonwealths shall only by this means attain perfect felicity, if either philosophers are kings, or kings give themselves to the study of philosophy, how far, I pray you, shall commonwealths then be from this felicity, if philosophers will not vouchsafe to instruct kings with their good counsel?"

"They are not so unkind," quoth he, "but they would gladly do it. Yea, many have done it already in books that they have put forth, if kings and princes would be willing and ready to follow good counsel. But Plato doubtless did well foresee that unless kings themselves would apply their minds to the study of philosophy, they would never thoroughly accept the counsel of philosophers, being themselves already even from their tender age infected, and corrupt with perverse and evil opinions. Which thing Plato himself proved true in King Dionysius.[17] If I should propose to any king wholesome decrees, endeavoring to pluck out of his mind the pernicious original causes of vice and worthlessness, think you not that I should forthwith either be driven away or else made a laughing stock? Go to, suppose that I were with the French king, and there sitting in his council, while in that most secret consultation, the king himself there being present in his own person, they beat their brains and search the very bottom of their wits to discuss by what crafty means the king may still keep Milan and draw back to him fugitive Naples,

[17] The reference is to Plato's vain effort to make a philosopher and wise ruler out of the young tyrant Dionysius II of Syracuse.

and then scheme how to conquer the Venetians, and bring under his jurisdiction all Italy, then how to win dominion over Flanders, Brabant, and all Burgundy, with divers other lands, whose kingdoms he has long ago in mind and purpose invaded. Here first one advises to conclude a league of peace with the Venetians, which shall endure as long as it be thought suitable and expedient for their purpose, and to take them also into their counsel, yea, and besides that to give them part of the prey, which, afterward, when they have accomplished their purpose after their own minds, they may demand back and claim again. Another thinks best to hire the Germans. Another would have the favor of the Swiss won with money. Another's advice is to appease the puissant power of the Emperor's majesty with gold, as a most pleasant and acceptable tribute. Meanwhile another proposes to make peace with the King of Aragon, and restore unto him his own kingdom of Navarre, as a full assurance of peace. Another comes in with his five eggs,[18] and advises to hook in the King of Castile with some hope of friendship or alliance, and to bring to their side certain peers of his court with great pensions.

"Meanwhile they all halt at the chief question of all, what to do in the meantime with England, and yet all agree in this

[18] An abbreviated form of an old English proverb, meaning to introduce a worthless or silly plan or to intrude with a bit of unsolicited suggestion. It occurs as "five eggs a penny and four of them addled," and "you come in with your five eggs a penny and four of them be rotten." The use of the proverb here is the work of Robinson, the translator, as there is nothing to correspond to it in More's Latin. But More would have been familiar with the phrase, for it was in common use in his day.

to make peace with the Englishmen, and with most sure and strong bonds to confirm that weak and feeble friendship, so that they shall be called friends, and held in suspicion as enemies. And therefore the Scots must be kept in readiness, as it were standing ready at all occasions, if peradventure the Englishmen should stir ever so little, instantly to set upon them. And moreover, privately and secretly (for openly it may not be done by the truce that is taken), privately, therefore, I say, they shall make much of some peer of England banished from his country, who must claim title to the crown of the realm and affirm himself just heir thereof, that by this subtle means they may hold the king bound to them, in whom else they have but small trust and confidence. Here I say, where so great and high matters are in consultation, where so many noble and wise men counsel their king only to war, here suppose I, a silly man, should rise up and urge them to turn over a leaf and learn a new lesson, saying that my advice is not to meddle with Italy, but to tarry still at home, and that the kingdom of France alone is almost greater than may well be governed by one man, and so the king should not need to study how to get more; and then should propose unto them the decrees of the people who are called the Achorians, who are situated over against the island of Utopia on the southeast side.

"These Achorians once made war in their king's quarrel to get him another kingdom, which he laid claim unto, and proclaimed himself rightful heir to the crown thereof, by the title of an old alliance. At last, when they had gotten it, they saw that they had quite as much vexation and trouble in keeping it as they had in getting it, and that either their new conquered subjects on sundry pretexts were making daily insurrections to rebel against, or else that other countries were continually with divers inroads and foragings invading them, and never could break up their camps. They saw themselves in the meantime despoiled and impoverished, their money carried out of the realm, their own men killed to maintain the glory of another nation. When they had no war, peace was no better than war, because their people in war had inured themselves to corrupt and wicked manners and had delight and pleasure in robbing and stealing. Through manslaughter they had gathered boldness for mischief, their laws were held in contempt, and nothing esteemed or regarded. Their king, being troubled with the charge and governance of two kingdoms, could not nor was able perfectly to discharge his office towards them both. Seeing again that all these evils and troubles were endless, they at last laid their heads together, and like faithful and loving subjects gave to their king free choice and liberty to keep whichever of these two kingdoms he would, alleging that he could not keep both, and that they were more than could well be governed by a king. For no man would be content to take him for his muleteer who kept another man's mules besides his. So this good prince was compelled to be content with his old kingdom and to surrender the new to one of his friends, who shortly after was violently driven out.

"If, furthermore, I should declare unto them that all this busy preparation for war, whereby many nations for his sake would be brought into a troublesome hurly-burly, all his coffers emptied, his treasures wasted, and his people destroyed, should at length through some mischance turn out to be vain and ineffectual; and that therefore it were best for him to content himself with his own kingdom of France, as his forefathers and predecessors did before him; to make much of it, to enrich it, and to make it as flourishing as he could; to exert himself to love his subjects, and again to be beloved of them, willingly to live with them, peaceably to govern them, and not to meddle with other kingdoms, seeing that which he has already is even enough for him, yea, and more than he can well turn his attention to: this my advice, Master More, how think you it would be heard and taken?"

"So God help me, not very thankfully," quoth I.

"Well, let us proceed then," quoth he. "Suppose that some king and his council were together whetting their wits and devising what subtle craft they might invent to enrich the king with great treasures of money. First one counsels to raise and enhance the valuation of money when the king must pay any; and again to reduce the value of coin to less than it is worth when he must receive or collect any. For thus great sums shall be paid with little money, and where little is due much shall be received.[19] Another advises to make a feint at waging war, so

[19] The first gold coins were issued in England in 1344, and for a century English currency remained relatively stable. But from the mid-fifteenth to the mid-sixteenth century, kings and their ministers learned to tamper with the currency as a means of meeting the demands made upon the royal treasury. Hence, debasement of the coinage had by More's time become one of the recognized evils of the day. Attempts at reform were made in the reign of Edward VI, but real reform did not come until 1561, after which time a sound currency became a contributing factor to Elizabethan prosperity.

that when under the color and pretense the king has gathered
great abundance of money, he may, when it shall please him,
make peace with great solemnity and holy ceremonies, to blind
the eyes of the poor commonalty, as if he were taking pity and
compassion, God wot, upon man's blood, like a loving and
merciful prince. Another puts the king in remembrance of certain old moth-eaten laws, that for a long time have not been
put in execution, which, because no man can remember that
they were made, every man has transgressed. He counsels the
king to exact fines for breaking these laws, for there is no way
so profitable or more honorable than that which has a show and
color of justice. Another advises him to forbid many things
under great penalties and fines, specially such things as it is for
the people's profit not to have practiced, and afterward to compensate with money those who by this prohibition sustain loss
and damage. For by this means the favor of the people is won,
and profit arises two ways: first by taking forfeits from them
whom covetousness of gain has brought in danger under this
statute, and, again, by selling privileges and licenses, which the
better the prince is, forsooth the dearer he sells them, as one who
is loath to grant to any private person anything that is against
the profit of his people. And therefore he may sell none but at an
exceedingly dear price.

"Another gives the king counsel to bring under his jurisdiction
the judges of the realm, that he may have them ever on his side,
and they must in every matter dispute and reason for the king's
right. And they must be called into the king's palace and be told
to argue and discuss his matters in his own presence. So there

shall be no case of his so openly and wrongly unjust, but that one or other of them, either because he will have something to allege and object, or because he is ashamed to say that which is said already, or else in order to seek favor with his prince, will not find some hole open to set a snare in, wherewith to trip up the other side. Thus while the judges cannot agree among themselves, reasoning and arguing of that which is plain enough, and bringing the manifest truth into doubt, meantime the king may seize the occasion to understand the law that shall most make for his advantage, unto which all others for shame or for fear will agree. Then the judges may be bold to pronounce for the king's side. For he that gives sentence for the king cannot be without a good excuse. For it shall be sufficient for him to have equity on his side, or the bare words of the law, or a twisted and distorted understanding of the same, or else (that which with good and just judges is of greater force than all the laws) the king's indisputable prerogative.

"To conclude, all the councilors agree and consent together with the rich Crassus that no abundance of gold can be sufficient for a prince, who must keep and maintain an army; furthermore that a king, even though he would, can do nothing unjustly. For all that all men have, yea also the men themselves are all his. And every man has as much of his own, as the king's gentleness has not taken from him. And it shall be most for the king's advantage that his subjects have very little or nothing in their possession, for his safeguard consists in this, that his people do not wax wanton and wealthy through riches and liberty, because where these things are, there men are not accustomed patiently to obey hard, unjust, and unlawful commandments; whereas under contrary conditions need and poverty hold down and keep under stout courages, and make them patient perforce, taking from them bold and rebelling stomachs.

"Here again, if I should rise up and boldly affirm that all these counsels are to the king's dishonor and reproach, since his honor and safety are more and rather supported and upholden by the wealth and riches of his people than by his own treasures; and if I should declare that the people choose their king for their own sake and not for his sake, to the intent, that through his labor and study they all may live wealthily, safe from wrongs and injuries, and that therefore the king ought to take more care for the wealth of his people than for his own wealth, even as the office and duty of a shepherd lie in that he is a shepherd, and should feed his sheep rather than himself.

"For as for their thinking that the defense and maintenance of peace depend on the poverty of the people, the facts themselves show that they are far out of the way. For where shall a man find more wrangling, quarreling, brawling, and chiding than among beggars? Who are more desirous of new mutations and alterations than they that are not content with the present state of their life? Or finally, who are bolder stomached to reduce all to a hurly-burly, thereby trusting to get some windfall, than they that have now nothing to lose? And if it should happen that there were any king so poorly regarded, so hated by his subjects, that he could keep them in awe only by open wrongs, by robbing and pillaging, and bringing them to beggary, surely it were better for him to forsake his kingdom than to hold it by this means, whereby, though the name of a king be kept, yet the majesty is lost. For it is against the dignity of a king to rule over beggars, rather than over rich and wealthy men. Of this mind was the hardy and courageous Fabricius, when he said that he had rather be a ruler of rich men than be rich himself. And verily, for one man to live in pleasure and wealth, while all others weep and smart for it, that is the part, not of a king, but of a jailer.[20]

"To be brief, as he is a foolish physician who cannot cure his patient's disease unless he cast him into another sickness, so he that cannot amend the lives of his subjects but by taking from them the wealth and comforts of life must needs admit that he knows not the art of governing free men. But let him amend his own life, renounce unhonest pleasures, and forsake pride. For these are the chief vices that cause him to incur the contempt or hatred of his people. Let him live of his own, hurting no man. Let him not spend more than he has. Let him restrain wickedness. Let him prevent vices, and take away the occasions of offenses, by ordering well his subjects, and not suffer wickedness to increase, to be afterward punished. Let him not be too hasty in reviving laws which custom has abrogated, especially such as have been long forgotten, and never missed or needed. And let him never under the cloak and pretense of transgression exact such fines and forfeits as no judge will suffer a private person to take, as unjust and full of guile.

[20] Throughout these sentences the word "wealth" is used in the sense of "well-being" rather than of "riches."

"Here I should describe to them the law of the Macariens, who are not far distant from Utopia, and whose king on the day of his coronation is bound by a solemn oath that he shall never at any time have in his treasure over a thousand pounds of gold or silver. They say that a very good king, who took more care for the wealth of his country than for the enriching of himself, made this law to be a check and bar to kings against heaping and hoarding up so much money as might impoverish their people. For he foresaw that this sum of treasure would suffice to support the king in battle against his own people, if they should chance to rebel, and also to maintain his wars against the invasions of foreign enemies. Further, he perceived that the same sum of money would be too little and insufficient to encourage and enable him wrongfully to take away other men's goods, which was the chief cause why the law was made. Another cause was this: he thought that by this provision his people should not lack money wherewith to maintain their daily business and traffic. And seeing the king could not choose but spend and bestow all that came in above the sum prescribed for him, he thought he would seek no occasions to do his subjects injury. Such a king shall be feared by evil men, and loved by good men. This and such other information, if I should offer to men wholly inclined and set in the contrary direction, how deaf hearers think you I should have?"

"Deaf hearers, doubtless," quoth I, "and in good faith no marvel. And to speak as I think, truly I cannot approve the offer of such information, or the giving of such counsel, as you are sure will never be regarded or received. For how can such

strange information be profitable, or how can it be beaten into
their heads, whose minds are already prejudiced with wholly
contrary persuasions? This school philosophy [21] is not unpleasant among friends in familiar conversation, but in the councils
of kings, where great matters are debated and reasoned with
great authority, these things have no place."

"That is what I meant," quoth he, "when I said philosophy
had no place among kings."

"Indeed," quoth I, "this school philosophy has not, which
thinks everything suitable for every place. But there is another
philosophy more civil, which knows, as you would say, her own
stage, and thereafter orders and behaves herself in the play
that she has in hand, playing her part accordingly with comeliness, uttering nothing out of due order and fashion. And this
is the philosophy that you must use. Or else while a comedy of
Plautus is playing, and the vile bondmen scoffing and trifling
among themselves, if you should suddenly come upon the stage
in a philosopher's apparel, and rehearse out of *Octavia* the place
where Seneca disputes with Nero, had it not been better for you
to have played the dumb person,[22] than by rehearsing that which
fitted neither the time nor the place, to have made such a tragical

[21] Reference is here made to the philosophy of the medieval schoolmen which, it
was held, might be all very well as an academic exercise among friends, but
would not suffice in a workaday world where practical decisions had to be made.
To some it may be suggestive of the modern idea that college professors are all
right in their place, but not as government advisers.

[22] The character who appears on the stage, but has no speaking part. The
comedies of Plautus depend in large part for their humor on the vulgar wit and
antics of slaves and freedmen. The tragedies of Seneca, of which *Octavia* is one,
treat of great personages, who speak in lofty and dignified language.

60

comedy or gallimaufry.[23] For by bringing in other stuff that appertains not at all to the present matter, you must needs mar and pervert the play that is in hand, even though the stuff you bring in be much better. What part soever you have taken upon you, play that as well as you can and make the best of it; and do not therefore disturb and throw out of order the whole affair because another, which is merrier and better, comes to your remembrance.

"So the case stands in a commonwealth, and so it is in the consultations of kings and princes. If evil opinions and naughty persuasions cannot be utterly and altogether plucked out of their hearts, if you cannot, even as you would, remedy vices which habit and custom have confirmed, yet this is no cause for leaving and forsaking the commonwealth. You must not forsake the ship in a tempest, because you cannot rule and keep down the winds. No, nor must you labor to drive into their heads new and strange information, which you know well will be all disregarded by those that are of wholly contrary minds. But you must with a crafty wile and subtle art endeavor, as much as in you lies, to handle the matter wisely and handsomely for the purpose, and that which you cannot turn to good, so order that it be not very bad. For it is not possible for all things to be well, unless all men are good—which I think will not be this good many years."

"By this means," quoth he, "nothing else will be brought to pass, but that while I go about to remedy the madness of others, I shall be even as mad as they. For if I would speak things that

[23] Originally a dish made of odds and ends of food; hence a confused jumble.

are true, I must needs speak such things. But as for speaking false things, whether that is a philosopher's part or no, I cannot tell; truly it is not my part. Howbeit, this talk of mine, though peradventure it may seem unpleasant to them, yet can I not see why it should seem strange, or foolishly newfangled. If indeed I should speak of those things that Plato imagined in his Republic, or that the Utopians do in theirs, these things, even though they were, as they are indeed, better, yet they might seem spoken out of place. Forasmuch as here amongst us, every man has his possessions separate to himself, and there all things are common. But what was contained in my talk that might not and ought not be spoken in any place? Save that to them who have thoroughly decreed and determined with themselves to drive headlong the contrary way, it cannot be acceptable and pleasant, because it calls them back, and shows them their dangers.

"Verily, if all the things that evil and vicious manners have caused to seem inconvenient and needless are to be rejected as things unsuitable and reproachful, then among Christian people we may wink at the most part of all the things which Christ taught us and strictly forbade to be winked at, that those things which he whispered in the ears of his disciples, he commanded should be proclaimed from the housetops. And yet most of them are more at variance with the manners of the world nowadays than my conversation was. But preachers, sly and wily men, following your counsel, as I suppose, because they saw men unwilling to frame their manners after Christ's rule, have twisted and perverted his doctrine, and like a rule of lead have applied it to men's manners, that by some means at least they might agree together. Whereby I cannot see what good they have done, except that men may with greater impunity be evil. And I truly should prevail just that much even in king's councils.

"For either I must say otherwise than they say, and then I might well say nothing, or else I must say the same that they say, and, as Mitio says in Terence, help further their madness. As for that crafty wile and subtle artifice of yours, I cannot perceive what purpose it serves, or why you would have me study and endeavor, if all things cannot be made good, yet to handle them wisely and handsomely for the purpose, that as far as possible they may not be very evil. For there is no place to dissemble or to wink in. Naughty counsels must be openly accepted and very pestilent decrees must be approved. He will be counted worse than a spy, yea almost as evil as a traitor, who with a faint heart praises evil and injurious decrees.

"Moreover, a man can have no opportunity to do good, falling into the company of those who will sooner ruin a good man than be made good themselves—through whose evil company he will be marred; or else, if he remain good and innocent, yet the wickedness and foolishness of others shall be imputed to him, and laid on his shoulders. So that it is impossible even with that crafty wile and subtle trickery to turn anything to better. Wherefore Plato in a goodly simile declares why wise men refrain from meddling in the commonwealth. For when they see the people swarming into the streets and daily wet to the skin with rain, and yet cannot persuade them to come in out of the rain and take to their houses, knowing well that if they should go out to them they would nothing prevail, nor win anything by it, but be wet also in the rain, they keep themselves within their houses, content to be safe themselves, seeing they cannot remedy the folly of the people.[24]

"Howbeit doubtless, Master More, to speak truly as my mind moves me, wheresoever possessions are private, where money wields all the influence, it is hard and almost impossible that there the commonwealth may justly be governed, and prosperously flourish. Unless you think that justice is there executed, where all things come into the hands of evil men; or that prosperity there flourishes where all is divided among a few; which few nevertheless do not live very richly, and the rest live miserably, wretched and beggarly. Wherefore I consider with myself and weigh in my mind the wise and godly ordinances of the Utopians, among whom with very few laws all things are so well and wealthily ordered, that virtue is properly rewarded and esteemed, and yet, all things being held there in common, every man has abundance of everything. Again, on the other hand, when I compare with them so many nations ever making new laws, yet not one of them all well and sufficiently furnished with laws; where every man calls what he has gotten his own proper and private goods; where the many new laws daily made are not sufficient for every man to enjoy, defend, and know from another man's that which he calls his own; which fact the infinite controversies in law, that daily arise and never are ended, plainly declare to be true.

[24] A free rendering of the passage in Plato's *Republic*, VI. See *Five Great Dialogues* Classics Club edition, p. 383.

"These things, I say, when I consider with myself, I hold well with Plato, and do not marvel that he would make no laws for them who refused the laws whereby all men should have and enjoy equal portions of wealth and commodities. For that wise man did easily foresee that this is the one and only way to the wealth of the community, that equality in all things should be set up and established. Which I think is not possible to maintain where every man's goods are proper and peculiar to himself. For where every man under certain titles and pretenses draws and grasps to himself as much as he can, and so a few divide among themselves all the riches there are, whatever may be the abundance and plenty, still to the rest are left lack and poverty. And for the most part it happens that this latter sort are more worthy to enjoy that state of wealth than the others are, because the rich men are covetous, crafty, and worthless. On the other part, the poor are lowly, simple, and by their daily labor more beneficial to the commonwealth than to themselves.

"Thus I do fully persuade myself that no equal and just distribution of things can be made, nor perfect wealth ever be among men unless their proprietorship be exiled and banished. But so long as it shall continue, so long shall remain among the most and best part of men the heavy and inevitable burden of poverty and wretchedness. Which, though I grant it may be somewhat eased, so I utterly deny that it can wholly be removed. For if there were a statute made that no man should have in his stock more than a prescribed and appointed sum of money; if it were by certain laws decreed that neither the king should be of too great power nor the people too proud and wealthy, and that offices should not be obtained by importunate suit, or by bribes and gifts; that they should neither be bought nor sold; that officials should not need to be at any cost or expense in their offices, for so excuse is given to them by fraud and greed to recoup themselves, and by reason of gifts and bribes the offices are given to rich men, which should rather have been filled by wise men: by such laws, I say, as sick bodies that are desperate and past cure are often with continual good cherishing kept alive, so these evils also might be lightened and mitigated. But that they might be perfectly cured, and brought to a good and upright state of health is not to be hoped for, while every man is master of his own to himself. Yea, and while you go about to cure one part, you make bigger the sore of another part; so the help of one causes another's harm; forasmuch as nothing can be given to any man unless it be taken from another."

"But I am of a contrary opinion," quoth I, "for methinks men shall never live wealthily there, where all things are held in common. For how can there be abundance of goods or of anything, where every man holds back his hand from labor? Where regard for his own gains drives him not to work, and the hope that he has in other men's toil makes him slothful. Then when they are pricked with poverty, and yet no man can by any law or right defend for his own that which he has got with the labor of his own hands, will not there of necessity be continual sedition and bloodshed? Especially since the authority and reverence of magistrates will be gone; for what place it can have with such men, among whom is no difference, I cannot devise."

"I marvel not," quoth he, "that you are of this opinion. For

,ou conceive in your mind either none at all, or else a very false image and picture of this thing. But if you had been with me in Utopia and had personally seen their fashions and laws, as I did, who lived there five years and more, and would never have come away, but only to make that new land known here, then doubtless you too would grant that you never saw people well ordered, but only there."

"Surely," quoth Master Peter, "it will be hard for you to make me believe that there is better order in that new land than is here in these countries that we know. For good wits are here as well as there, and I think our commonwealths are ancienter than theirs; and in them long use and experience have found out many things beneficial to man's life, besides the many things here among us that have been discovered by chance, which no wit could ever have devised."

"As touching ancientness," quoth he, "of commonwealths, you might better judge, if you had read the histories and chronicles of that land, where if we may believe them, cities were there before there were men here. And whatsoever thing hitherto has been devised by wit, or found by chance, that might as well be there as here. But I think, verily, though it may be that we did surpass them in wit, yet in study and laborsome endeavor they far surpass us. For, as their chronicles testify, before our arrival there they had never heard anything of us, whom they call the ultra-equinoctials, save that once, about 1200 years ago, a ship was lost off the isle of Utopia, which was driven thither by tempest. Certain Romans and Egyptians were cast on land, who after that never went from there. Mark now what profit they took of this one occasion through diligence and earnest travail. There was no craft or science within the empire of Rome wherefrom any profit could rise, but they either learned it from these strangers, or else made use of them to search for it, and find it out for themselves. So great a profit was it to them that they never left their country. But if any like chance before now has brought any man from there hither, it is quite lost to remembrance, as it also perchance in time to come shall be forgotten that ever I was there. And though they quickly, almost at the first meeting, made their own whatever advantageous devices exist among us, I suppose it would be long before we would receive anything that among them is better instituted than among us. And this, I suppose, is the chief cause why their commonwealths are wiselier governed and flourish in more wealth than ours, though neither in wit nor riches are we their inferiors."

"Therefore, gentle Master Raphael," quoth he, "I pray you and beseech you to describe unto us that island. And aim not to be short, but declare at length in order their lands, their rivers, their cities, their people, their manners, their ordinances, their laws, and, in short, all things that you think us desirous to know. And you shall think us desirous to know whatsoever we know not yet."

"There is nothing," quoth he, "that I will gladlier do. For all these things I have fresh in mind. But the matter requires leisure."

"Let us go in, therefore," quoth I, "to dinner. Afterward we will spend the time as we please."

"Content," quoth he; "be it."

So we went in and dined. When dinner was done, we came into the same place again, and sat us down upon the same bench, commanding our servants that no man should trouble us. Then I and Master Peter Giles desired Master Raphael to perform his promise. He, therefore, seeing us desirous and willing to hearken to him, when he had sat still and paused a little while, musing and bethinking himself, thus began to speak.

THE END OF THE FIRST BOOK.

THE SECOND BOOK

The Second Book of the Conversation of Raphael Hythloday, concerning the best state of a Commonwealth, containing the description of Utopia, with a large declaration of the politic government, and all the good laws and orders of the same Island.

Ｔ HE ISLAND of Utopia contains in breadth in the middle part of it (for there it is broadest) two hundred miles. Which breadth continues through the most part of the land, save that little by little it comes in and waxes narrow towards both ends, which forming a circuit or compass of five hundred miles fashions the whole island like to the new moon. Between these two corners the sea runs in, dividing them asunder by a distance of eleven miles or thereabouts, and there spreads out into a large and wide sea, which by reason that the land on every side compasses it about, and shelters it from the winds, is not rough, nor mounts with great waves, but flows almost quietly, not much unlike a great standing pool; and makes almost all the space within the heart of the land like a haven, and to the great convenience of the inhabitants receives ships bound towards every part of the land. The forefronts or frontiers of the two corners, what with shallows and ᵣeefs and what with rocks, are very jeopardous and dangerous.

In the middle between them both stands up above the water a great rock, which is not perilous because it is in sight. Upon the top of this rock is a fair and strong tower built, which they hold with a garrison of men. Other rocks there are that lie hid under the water, and therefore are dangerous. The channels are known only to themselves. And therefore it seldom chances that any stranger, unless he be guided by a Utopian, can come into this haven. Insomuch that they themselves could scarcely enter without danger if their way were not directed and ruled by certain landmarks standing on the shore. By turning, transferring, and removing these marks into other places they may destroy their enemies' navies, be they never so many. The outer side of the land is also full of havens, but the landing is so surely defended, both by nature and by workmanship of man's hand, that a few defenders may drive back many armies. Howbeit, as they say, and as the fashion of the place does partly show, it was ever the sea that compassed it about. But King Utopus, whose name as conqueror the island bears (for before that time it was called Abraxa), who also brought the rude and wild people to that excellent perfection in all good fashions, humanity, and civil gentleness, wherein they now surpass all the people of the world,—even at his first arriving and entering upon the land, forthwith obtaining the victory, caused fifteen miles of upland ground, where the sea had no passage, to be cut and dug up, and so brought the sea round to the land. He set to this work not only the inhabitants of the island, that they should

not think it done in contumely and despite, but also all of **his** own soldiers. Thus the work, being divided among so great a number of workmen, was with exceeding, marvelous speed despatched. Insomuch that the neighboring people who at the first began to mock, and to jest at this vain enterprise, then turned their laughter to marvel at the success, and to fear.

There are in the island fifty-four large and fair cities, or shire towns, agreeing all together in one tongue, like manners, institutions, and laws. They are all set and situate alike, and in all points fashioned alike, as far as the place or plot permits. Of these cities they that are nearest together are twenty-four miles apart. Again, there is none of them distant from the next more than one day's journey afoot. There come yearly to Amaurote out of every city three old men, wise and well experienced, there to treat and debate of the common matters of the land. For this city (because it stands just in the midst of the island, and is therefore most meet for the ambassadors of all parts of the realm) is taken for the chief and head city. The precincts and bounds of the shires are so conveniently appointed and marked out for the cities that never a one of them all has less than twenty miles of ground on every side, and in places also much more, as in that part where the cities are farthest.

None of the cities desires to enlarge the bounds and limits of its shires, for they count themselves rather the good farmers than the owners of their lands. They have built in the country, in all parts of the shire, houses or farms well appointed and furnished with all sorts of farming implements and tools.

These houses are inhabited by the citizens, who come thither to dwell in turn. No household or farm in the country has fewer than forty persons, men and women, besides two bondmen,[1] who are all under the rule and order of the goodman and goodwife of the house, both very sage and discreet persons. And every thirty farms or families have one head ruler, who is called a *philarch,* being as it were a head bailiff. Out of every one of these families or farms come every year into the city twenty persons who have been two years in the country. In their place so many fresh are sent thither out of the city, to be instructed and taught by those who have been there a year already, and are therefore expert and skilled in the care and cultivation of the land. And they the next year shall teach the others. This order is kept for fear that either scarceness of victuals, or some other like misfortune should result from lack of knowledge, if they were altogether new, and fresh, and unexpert in farming.

This manner and fashion of yearly changing and renewing those engaged in farming, though it be customary and regularly followed, to the intent that no man shall be constrained against his will to continue long in that hard and sharp kind of life, yet many of them take such pleasure and delight in

1 See p. 127 for More's explanation of the bondmen in Utopia. The term was currently applied to the serf or villein at the bottom of the scale in manorial society, who as a "baseborn" person was obligated to remain on the land and to perform certain onerous services for his lord. By More's time this sort of bondage was rare in England, though it still flourished in many places on the Continent, and occasional examples of English bondmen are found as late as the seventeenth century.

the work on the land that they remain a longer space of years. These farmers plow and till the ground, and breed cattle, and make ready wood, which they carry to the city either by land, or by water, as they may most conveniently. They bring up a multitude of poultry, and that by a marvelous device. For the hens do not sit upon the eggs, but the farmers by keeping them in a certain even heat bring life into them, and hatch them. The chickens, as soon as they come out of the shell, follow men and women instead of the hens. They raise very few horses; and none but very fierce ones, and for no other use or purpose but only to exercise their youth in riding and feats of arms. For oxen are put to all the labor of plowing and drawing, which they grant are not so good as horses at a sudden spurt, and, as we say, at lifting a dead weight. Yet they hold the opinion that they will endure and suffer much more labor and pain than horses will. And they think that oxen are not in danger and subject to so many diseases, and that they are kept and maintained with much less cost and charge; and finally that they are good for meat, when they are past labor.

They sow corn only for bread. For their drink is either wine made of grapes, or else of apples or of pears; or else it is clean water.[2] And many times mead is made of honey or liquorice

[2] More's approval of water for drinking, provided it were clean, places him in advance of his contemporaries in matters of hygiene as well as in other fields; for most of the writers of the sixteenth century who ventured advice on health and diet warned particularly of the danger of drinking water. The other drinks he mentions were all popular at the time in England. That made from the juice of pears was commonly called 'Perry.' Mead, made of four parts of water to one

boiled in water, for thereof they have great store. And though they know certainly—for they know it perfectly indeed—how much victuals the city with the whole country or shire round about it uses, yet they sow much more corn, and breed up much more cattle than serves for their own use, and the overplus they divide among their neighbors. Whatsoever necessary things are lacking in the country, all such stuff they fetch out of the city; where without any exchange they easily obtain it from the magistrates of the city. For every month many of them go into the city on the holy day. When their harvest day draws near and is at hand, then the philarchs, who are the head officers and bailiffs on the farms, send word to the magistrates of the city what number of harvest men is needful to be sent to them out of the city. And this company of harvest men are there ready at the day appointed, and almost in one fair day despatch all the harvest work.

Of the cities, and namely, of Amaurote

As for their cities, he that knows one of them knows them all, for all are as like one to another, as the nature of the place permits. I will describe therefore to you one or another of them, for it matters not greatly which; but what one is better than Amaurote? Of them all this is the worthiest and of most dignity. For the rest acknowledge it as the head city, because

---

of fermented honey, was a milder drink than its famous medieval predecessor *metheglin*, in which only two parts of water to one of honey were used.

there is the council house. Nor is any of them all better be-loved by me, as I lived therein five whole years together. The city of Amaurote stands upon the side of a low hill, in fashion almost foursquare. For the breadth of it begins a little beneath the top of the hill, and still continues for the space of two miles, until it comes to the river of Anyder. The length of it, which lies by the river's side, is somewhat more. The river of Anyder rises twenty-four miles above Amaurote out of a little spring. But being increased by other small floods and brooks that run into it—among others, two somewhat big ones —opposite the city it is a half mile broad, and farther broader. And sixty miles beyond the city it falls into the Ocean sea. Through all that space that lies between the sea and the city, and a good number of miles also above the city, the water ebbs and flows six hours together with a swift tide. When the sea flows in, for the length of thirty miles it fills all the Anyder with salt water, and drives back the fresh water of the river. And somewhat further it taints the sweetness of the fresh water with saltness. But a little beyond that the river waxes sweet, and runs past the city fresh and pleasant. And when the sea ebbs, and goes back again, the fresh water follows it almost even to the very fall into the sea.

There goes a bridge over the river, made not of piles of timber but of stonework, with gorgeous and substantial arches at that part of the city that is farthest from the sea, to the in-tent that ships may pass along all the side of the city without hindrance. They have also another river which indeed is not very great, but it runs gently and pleasantly. For it rises even out of the same hill that the city stands upon, and runs down a slope through the midst of the city into Anyder. And because it rises a little outside the city, the Amaurotians have enclosed the head spring of it with strong fences and bulwarks, and so have joined it to the city. This is done to the intent that the water should not be stopped, or turned away, or poisoned, if their enemies should chance to come upon them. From thence the water is diverted in all directions and brought down in canals of brick divers ways into the lower parts of the city. Where that cannot be done, because the place will not allow it, there they gather the rain water in great cisterns, which does them as good service.[3]

The city is compassed about with a high and thick wall full of turrets and bulwarks. A dry ditch, but deep and broad, and overgrown with bushes, briers, and thorns, surrounds three sides or quarters of the city. To the fourth side the river itself serves for a ditch. The streets are laid out very conveniently and handsomely, both for transport, and also against the winds. The houses are of fair and gorgeous building, and on the street side they stand joined together in a long row through the

[3] More has made his Amaurote enough like London to be recognizable, lying as it does by "the river's side," with its conduits, and its one bridge made of stone, supplied with a drawbridge that could be raised when large ships went through. In fact, the Elizabethan, John Stow, who knew his London well, says that More's description "doth in every particular thing so exactly square and correspond with our city of London that I make little doubt that writer did thereby mean the same place." But it is obvious in the succeeding paragraph that it was London as More wished it to be rather than as it was; for the Utopian city far surpassed his own in matters of sanitation, width of streets, and other features of city planning. London streets, as he knew them, were only ten to twelve feet wide.

whole street, without any partition or separation. The streets are twenty feet broad. On the back side of the houses through the whole length of the street lie large gardens which are closed in round about by the back part of the streets. Every house has two doors, one into the street, and a postern door on the back side into the garden. These doors are made with two leaves, never locked or bolted, so easy to be opened that they will follow the least drawing of a finger, and shut again by themselves. Every man that wills may go in, for there is nothing within the houses that is private or any man's own.[4] And every tenth year they change their houses by lot.

They set great store by their gardens. In them they have vineyards, all manner of fruit, herbs, and flowers, so pleasant, so well planted and so finely kept that I never saw anything more fruitful or better trimmed in any place. Their study and diligence herein comes not only from pleasure, but also from a certain strife and rivalry that is between street and street, concerning the trimming, tilling, and furnishing of their gardens, every man for his own part. And verily you shall not lightly find in all the city anything that is better arranged, either for the profit of the citizens, or for pleasure. And therefore it may seem that the first founder of the city cared for

[4] Here, as often in the following pages, one is aware of More's great debt to the classical authors, whose works he had diligently studied. It is especially natural that Plato's ideal commonwealth should come often to mind as he set about the task of fashioning his own. On the final page of the third book of the *Republic*, are these words: "None of them [the citizens] should have any property beyond what is absolutely necessary; neither should they have a private house with bars and bolts closed against anyone who has a mind to enter." (See Plato, *Five Great Dialogues*, Classics Club edition, p. 305.)

nothing so much as he did for these gardens.[5] For they say that King Utopus himself, even at the first beginning, appointed and drew the ground plan of the city in the fashion and figure that it has now, but the handsome garnishing, and the beautiful setting forth of it, for which he saw that one man's age would not suffice, that he left to his posterity.

For their chronicles, which they keep written with all diligent circumspection, containing the history of 1760 years, even from the first conquest of the island, record and witness that the houses in the beginning were very low, and like homely cottages or poor shepherd houses built in haphazard fashion of every rude piece of wood that came first to hand, with mud walls and ridged roofs, thatched over with straw. But now the houses are elaborately built, in a gorgeous and ornate style, with three stories one over another. The outsides of the walls are made either of hard flint, or of plaster, or else of brick, and the inner sides are well strengthened with timber work. The roofs are plain and flat, covered with a certain kind of plaster that is of no cost, and yet so tempered that no fire can hurt or destroy it, and it withstands the violence of the weather

[5] More is not writing here as a satirist, but with the ardor ever displayed by a true-born Englishman when the talk is of gardens. London was spoken of as early as the twelfth century as a "city of gardens." In More's time and throughout the Tudor period the wealthier classes were developing large gardens of somewhat formal design, showing a marked Italian influence. Francis Bacon's essay, "Of Gardens" tells how to plant one of these large and elaborate gardens. (See Classics Club edition of Bacon's *Essays*, p. 190.) Outside of London, nobility and gentry vied with each other in adorning their estates. Nor was it an art limited to the upper classes, for the homes of farmers and tradesmen were brightened by tiny but well-ordered gardens.

better than any lead. They keep the wind out of their **windows** with glass, for it is there much used,[6] or in some places with fine linen cloth dipped in oil or resin of amber, a convenience in two ways; for by this means more light comes in, and the wind is better kept out.

Of the magistrates

Every thirty families or farms choose yearly an officer, who in their old language is called the *syphogrant,* and by a newer name, the *philarch*. Every ten syphogrants, with their 300 families are under an officer who was once called the *tranibore,* now the chief philarch. Moreover, as concerning the election of the prince, all the syphogrants, who are in number 200, first are sworn to choose him whom they think most fitting and expedient. Then by a secret election they name prince one of those four whom the people before named unto them. For out of the four quarters of the city there are four chosen, out of every quarter one, to stand for the election, which is put up to the council. The prince's office continues all his lifetime, unless he is deposed or put down for suspicion of tyranny. They choose the tranibores yearly, but do not lightly change them. All the other offices are but for one year. The tranibores

[6] Here the Utopians were again far ahead of the English. In 1602, window glass in the homes of private individuals was still spoken of as a "late introduction," and it was not until the end of the seventeenth century that it was a commonplace in the homes of the poorer classes.

every third day, and sometimes, if need be, oftener, come into the council house with the prince. Their council is concerning the commonwealth. If there are any controversies among the commoners, which are very few, they despatch and end them speedily. They take always two syphogrants with them in counsel, and every day a new couple. And it is provided that nothing touching the commonwealth shall be confirmed and ratified unless it has been reasoned and debated three days in the council before it is decreed. To have any consultation for the commonwealth outside the council, or the place of the common election, is punishable by death. This statute, they say, was made to the intent that the prince and tranibores might not easily conspire together to oppress the people by tyranny, and to change the state of the commonwealth.

Therefore matters of great weight and importance are brought to the election house of the syphogrants, who explain the matter to their families. And afterward, when they have consulted among themselves, they report their plan to the council. Sometimes the matter is brought before the council of the whole island. Furthermore this custom also the council observes: to dispute or reason of no matter the same day that it is first proposed or put forth, but to defer it to the next sitting of the council, in order that no man, when he has rashly there spoken what came first to his tongue's end, shall then afterward study rather for reasons wherewith to defend and confirm his first foolish sentence than for the good of the commonwealth: as one more willing to suffer harm or hindrance to the commonwealth than any loss or diminution of his own reputation; and as one that would not for shame (which is a very foolish shame) appear to have been misled in the matter at the first, when at the first he ought to have spoken rather wisely, than hastily, or rashly.

Of sciences, crafts, and occupations

Agriculture is a science common to them all in general, both men and women, wherein they are all expert and cunning. In this they are all instructed, even from their youth, partly in schools with traditions and precepts, and partly in the country nigh the city, brought up as it were in playing, not only to behold the use of it, but for the sake of exercising their bodies to practice it also. Besides farming which, as I said, is common to them all, every one of them learns one or another distinct and particular skill, as his own proper craft. That is most commonly either clothworking in wool or flax, or masonry, or the smith's craft, or the carpenter's craft. For there is no other occupation that any number to speak of follows there. For their garments, which throughout all the island are of one fashion (save that there is a difference between the man's garment and the woman's, between the married and the unmarried) continue forevermore unchanged. They are seemly and comely to the eye, permitting free movement and exercise of the body, and are also fit both for winter and summer. As for these garments, I say, every family makes their own. But of the other aforesaid crafts every man learns one.

And not only the men, but also the women. But the women, as the weaker sort, are put to the easier crafts; they work wool and flax. The other more laborsome skills are committed to the men. For the most part every man is brought up in his father's craft. For most commonly they are naturally thereto bent and inclined. But if a man's mind turn to any other, he is by adoption put into a family of that occupation which he does most fancy; and not only his father, but also the magistrates do diligently look to him, that he be put with a discreet and an honest householder. Yea, and if any person, when he has learned one craft, is desirous to learn another also, he is likewise permitted. When he has learned both, he follows whichever he will, unless the city has more need of the one than of the other.

The chief and almost the only office of the syphogrants is to see and take heed that no man sit idle, but that everyone ply his own craft with earnest diligence. And yet for all that, not to be wearied from early in the morning to late in the evening with continual work, like laboring and toiling beasts. For this is worse than the miserable and wretched condition of bondmen, but it is nevertheless almost everywhere the life of workmen and artisans, save in Utopia. For they, dividing the day and the night into twenty-four equal hours, appoint and assign only six of those hours to work, three before noon, after which they go straight to dinner; and after dinner, when they have rested two hours, then they work three, and upon that they go to supper. After eight of the clock in the evening, counting one of the clock as the first hour after noon, they

83

go to bed; eight hours they give to sleep.[7] All the spare time, that is, between the hours of work, sleep, and meat, they are permitted to spend every man as he likes best himself. Not to the intent that they should misspend this time in riot or slothfulness, but that being then freed from the labor of their own occupations, they should bestow the time well and thriftily upon some other good science, as shall please them. For it is a regular custom there, to have lectures daily, early in the morning, where only those are constrained to be present that are chosen and appointed to learning. Howbeit a great multitude of every sort of people, both men and women, go to hear lectures, some to one and some to another, as every man's nature is inclined. Yet, this notwithstanding, if any man had rather bestow this time upon his own occupation, as it chances with many, whose minds rise not to the contemplation of any liberal science, he is not prevented or prohibited, but is also praised and commended, as being profitable to the commonwealth. After supper they spend one hour in play, in summer in their gardens, in winter in their common halls, where they dine and sup. There they exercise themselves in music, or else in honest and wholesome conversation. Diceplay, and such other foolish and pernicious games, they know not.

[7] In 1514, only two years before More published the *Utopia*, Parliament re-enacted with very slight modification the Statute of 1495 controlling the hours of English laborers. According to this law, from mid-March to mid-September, every worker should be at his work from "before five o'clock in the morning" until "seven or eight o'clock in the evening." During the remainder of the year the work day was to be from daylight to dark. It is small wonder that More's proposal of a six-hour day, not yet attained in our own time, seemed revolutionary.

BOOK TWO

But they play two games not unlike chess. The one is the battle of numbers, wherein one number steals away another. The other is one wherein vices fight with virtues, as it were in battle array, or a set field. In this game is very properly shown both the strife and discord that vices have among themselves, and again their unity and concord against virtues. And also what vices are repugnant to what virtues, with what power and strength they assail them openly, by what wiles and subtlety they assault them secretly, with what help and aid the virtues resist and overcome the power of the vices, by what craft they frustrate their purpose, and finally by what cunning or means the one gets the victory.[8]

But here, lest you be deceived, one thing you must look more narrowly upon. For seeing they bestow but six hours in work, perchance you may think that a lack of some necessary things may ensue therefrom. But this is not so. For that short time is not only enough but even too much for the store and abundance of all things that are requisite, either for the necessity or the comfort of life. And this you also shall perceive, if you weigh and consider with yourselves how great a part of the people in other countries live idle. First, almost all women, who are half of the whole number; or else if the women be anywhere occupied, there most commonly in their stead the men are idle. Besides this how great and how idle a

[8] In advocating the use of games as a means of education, More was not only in agreement with Plato (*Laws*, Book I, 643), but with some of the most renowned Renaissance educators.

The "battle of numbers" was sometimes called the "philosopher's game." It is described in various works dealing with early sports and pastimes.

company is there of priests and religious men,[9] as they call them. Add thereto all rich men, especially all landed men, who are commonly called gentlemen and noblemen. Take into this number also their servants: I mean all that flock of stout bragging swashbucklers. Join to them also the sturdy and lusty beggars, cloaking their idle life under the color of some disease or sickness. And truly you shall find them much fewer than you thought, by whose labor all things are gotten that men use and live by. Next consider with yourself, of these few that do work, how few are occupied in necessary works. For where money is everything, there must needs be many vain and superfluous occupations, to serve only for riotous superfluity and unhonest pleasure. For the same multitude that now is occupied in work, if they were divided into as few occupations as the necessary use of nature requires, so great plenty of things of necessity would be produced that doubtless the prices would be too little for the workers to maintain their livings. But if all these that are now busied about unprofitable occupations, with all the whole flock of them that now live idly and slothfully, who consume and waste every one of them more of the things that come by other men's labor than two of the workmen themselves do; if all these, I say, were set to profitable occupations, you easily perceive how little time would

[9] The reference here is to members of the various religious orders. The monks had, through the profligate living of some of their number, lost the popular esteem and affection felt for them earlier, and their idleness and extravagance were subjects of common complaint in the literature of the time. This feeling accounts in large measure for the amount of support given in 1539 to the dissolution of the monasteries.

be enough, yea and too much, to supply us with all things that may be requisite either for necessity, or for comfort, yea or for pleasure, so long as that pleasure is genuine and natural.

And in Utopia the condition makes this manifest and plain. For there, in all the city, with the whole country or shire adjoining to it, scarcely 500 persons of the whole number of men and women, who are neither too old nor too weak to work, are freed from labor. Among them are the syphogrants who (though they are by the laws exempt and privileged from labor) yet exempt not themselves, to the intent they may the rather by their example incite others to work. The same vacation from labor is also enjoyed by those to whom the people, persuaded by the commendation of the priests and the secret election of the syphogrants, have given a perpetual freedom from labor for learning. But if any one of them prove not equal to the expectation and hope conceived of him, he is forthwith plucked back into the company of artisans. And contrariwise, often it chances that a handicraftsman does so earnestly bestow his vacant and spare hours in learning, and through diligence so profits therein that he is taken from his manual occupation, and promoted to the company of the learned. Out of this order of the learned are chosen ambassadors, priests, tranibores, and finally the prince himself, whom they in their old tongue call Barzanes, and by a newer name, Adamus. The residue of the people being neither idle nor occupied about unprofitable exercises, it may easily be judged in how few hours how much good work can be done by them towards those things that I have spoken of. This advantage they have also above others, that in most of the necessary occupations they need not do as much work as other nations do.

For first of all the building or repairing of houses demands everywhere else so many men's continual labor, because the unthrifty heir suffers the houses that his father built to fall in time in decay; so that which he might have maintained with little cost, his successor is constrained to build again anew, to his great charge. Yea, many times also a house cost one man much money, but another is of so nice and so delicate a mind that he thinks nothing of it; and it being neglected, and therefore shortly falling into ruin, he builds up another in another place with no less cost and charge. But among the Utopians, where all things are set up in good order, and where the commonwealth is on a good foundation, it very seldom chances that they choose a new plot to build a house upon. And they do not only make speedy and quick repairs of present weaknesses, but also preserve them that are like to fall. And by this means their houses endure and last very long with little labor and small repairs; insomuch that this kind of workmen sometimes have almost nothing to do. But they are commanded to hew timber at home, and to square and trim up stones, to the intent that if any work arise, it may the speedier be taken care of.

Now, sir, for their apparel, mark, I pray you, how few workmen they need. First of all, while they are at work they are plainly clad in leather or skins that will last seven years. When they go forth abroad they cast over them a cloak which hides the other plain apparel. These cloaks throughout the whole island are all of one color, and that is the natural color of the wool. They therefore do not only use much less woolen cloth than is used in other countries, but also the same stands them in much less cost. But linen cloth is made with less labor, and is therefore more in use. But in linen cloth only whiteness, in woolen only cleanliness is regarded. As for the thinness or fineness of the thread, that is not considered important. Yet this is the cause why in other places four or five cloth gowns of divers colors, and as many silk coats, are not enough for one man. Yea, and if he be of a particular and nice sort, ten are too few; whereas there one garment will serve a man most commonly two years. For why should he desire more? Seeing if he had them, he would not be the better wrapped or covered from the cold, nor in his apparel any whit handsomer. Wherefore, seeing they are all exercised in profitable occupations, and that a few workers in the same crafts are sufficient, and for this cause plenty of everything being among them, they do sometimes bring out an innumerable company of people to mend the highways, if any are broken. Many times also, when they have no such work to be occupied about, a public proclamation is made, that they shall spend fewer hours in work. For the magistrates do not exercise their citizens against their wills in unnecessary labors. And why? In the institution of that commonwealth, this end only is aimed at and minded, that whatever time may possibly be spared from the necessary occupations and affairs of the commonwealth, all

that, the citizens should withdraw from manual labor and
apply to the free liberty of the mind, and to cultivating the
same. For herein they suppose the felicity of this life to consist.

Of their living and mutual intercourse together

But now will I declare how the citizens bear themselves one
towards another, what familiar intercourse there is among the
people, and what fashion they employ in distributing everything. First, the city consists of families, the families most
commonly composed of kindred. For the women, when they
are married at a lawful age, go into their husbands' houses. But
the male children with all the whole male offspring continue
still in their own family and are governed by the eldest and
ancientest father, unless he becomes a dotard; for then the
next to him in age is put in his place. But to the intent the prescribed number of citizens should neither decrease, nor above
measure increase, it is ordained that no city, including its out-
skirts, shall have more than six thousand families, and that
no family shall include fewer than ten or more than sixteen
grown children, that is, of the age of fourteen or above. There
is no rule for children under this age. This measure or number is easily observed and kept, by putting those that in too
full families are above the number into families of smaller increase. But if it chance that in the whole city the population
increase above the just number, they fill up therewith the lack

of other cities. But if it happen that the multitude throughout the whole island pass and exceed the due number, then they choose out of every city certain citizens, and build up a town under their own laws in the next land where the inhabitants have much waste and unoccupied ground, also some of the inhabitants among them, if they will join and dwell with them. Thus joining and dwelling together, they do easily agree on one fashion of living, and that to the great wealth of both peoples. For they so bring the matter about by their laws, that the ground which before was neither good nor profitable for the one or for the other, is now sufficient and fruitful enough for them both.

But if the inhabitants of that land will not dwell with them, to be ordered by their laws, then they drive them out of those bounds which they have limited and defined for themselves. And if they resist and rebel, then they make war against them. For they count this the most just cause of war, when any people holds a piece of ground void and vacant, to no good or profitable use, keeping others from the use and possession of it, who, notwithstanding the law of nature, ought to be nourished and supported thereon.[10] If any chance do so much diminish the

[10] It is interesting to compare More's views here with those of the Dutch jurist Grotius, who wrote in the next century. His work *On the Law of War and Peace* (1626) contains the following: "If within the territory of a people there is any deserted and unproductive soil, this also ought to be granted to foreigners, if they ask for it. Or it is right for foreigners even to take possession of such ground, for the reason that uncultivated land ought not to be considered as occupied except in respect to sovereignty, which remains unimpaired in favour of the original people." (Book II, ch. II, sec. 17, Scott edition.) The passage is also somewhat suggestive of the ideas later set forth by Henry George.

numbers in any of their cities that it cannot be filled up again, without the diminishing of the just number in the other cities (which they say chanced but twice since the beginning of the land through a great pestilent plague), then they make up the number with citizens fetched out of their own foreign towns, for they had rather suffer their foreign towns [11] to decay and perish than any city of their own island to be diminished.

But now again to the intercourse of the citizens among themselves. The eldest, as I said, rules the family. The wives are ministers to their husbands, the children to their parents, and, to be short, the younger to their elders. Every city is divided into four equal parts. In the midst of every quarter there is a market place for all manner of things. Thither the produce of every family is brought into certain houses. And every kind of thing is laid up in the severa' barns or store houses. From hence the father of every family, or every householder, takes whatsoever he and his have need of, and carries it away with him without money, without exchange, without any security. For why should anything be denied him? Seeing there is abundance of all things, and that it is not to be feared that any man will ask for more than he needs. For why should it be thought that a man would ask for more than enough, who is sure never to lack? Certainly in all kinds of living creatures, fear of lack causes covetousness and greed; in man also pride, which counts it a glorious thing to surpass and excel others in

11 That is, the towns on the nearest mainland that had been settled by people from Utopia.

the superfluous and vain ostentation of things. But this kind
of vice among the Utopians can have no place.

Next to the market places that I spoke of, stand the food
markets, whither are brought not only all sorts of herbs, and
fruits of trees, with bread, but also fish, and all manner of
four-footed beasts, and wild fowl that are man's meat. But
first the filthiness and ordure thereof are clean washed away
in the running river outside the city in places appointed for
the same purpose. From thence the beasts are brought in killed,
and clean washed by the hands of the bondmen. For they permit not their free citizens to accustom themselves to the killing of beasts, through which practice they think that clemency,
the gentlest affection of our nature, little by little decays and
perishes.[12] Neither do they permit anything that is filthy,
loathsome, or uncleanly to be brought into the city, lest the air
by the stench thereof, infected and corrupt, should cause pestilent diseases.

Moreover every street has certain great large halls set an equal
distance one from another, every one known by its own name.
In these halls dwell the syphogrants. And to every one of the
same halls are appointed thirty families, fifteen on either side.
The stewards of every hall at a certain hour come into the meat
markets, where they receive meat according to the number of
their halls.

But first and chiefly of all, respect is paid to the sick, that
are in the hospitals. For in the circuit of the city, a little be-

[12] See footnote on p. 117.

yond the walls, they have four hospitals, so big, so wide, so ample, and so large that they may seem four little towns, which were planned of that size partly to the intent that the sick, be they never so many in number, should not lie too crowded, and therefore uneasily and uncomfortably; and partly in order that they who are taken and suffering with contagious diseases, such as are wont by infection to creep from one to another, might be laid apart from the company of the rest. These hospitals are so well appointed, and so furnished with all things necessary to health, and moreover such diligent attention is given through the continual presence of skilful physicians, that though no man is sent thither against his will, yet still there is no sick person in all the city who had not rather lie there than at home in his own house.[13]

When the steward of the sick has received such meats as the physicians have prescribed, then the best is equally divided among the halls, according to the company in every one, save that there respect is paid to the prince, the bishop, the tranibores, and to ambassadors and all strangers, if there are any, which is seldom. But they also when they are there have certain houses appointed and prepared for them. To these halls at the set hours of dinner and supper come all the whole syphogranty or ward, called by the noise of a brazen trumpet, except such as are sick in the hospitals, or else in their own

[13] Hospitals in England in More's day were under the direction of the religious orders and functioned more often as almshouses than as places for medical treatment. A notable exception was St. Bartholomew's in London, which from its foundation in 1123 had been chiefly concerned with the care of the sick. It received a new charter under Henry VIII.

houses. Howbeit, no man is prohibited or forbidden, after the hails are served, to fetch home meat out of the market to his own house, for they know that no man will do it without a reasonable cause. For though no man is prohibited to dine at home, yet no man does it willingly, because it is counted an act of small honor. And also it were folly to take the pains to prepare a bad dinner at home, when they may be welcome to good and fine fare so nigh at hand in the hall.

In this hall all menial service, all slavery, and drudgery, with all laborsome toil and business, are done by bondmen. But the women of every family in turn have the office and charge of cookery for boiling and dressing the meat, and ordering all things belonging thereto. They sit at three tables or more, according to the number of their company. The men sit upon the bench next the wall, and the women opposite them on the other side of the table, so that if any sudden evil should chance to them, as many times happens to women with child, they may rise without trouble or disturbance of anybody, and go thence to the nursery. The nurses sit separately alone with their young sucklings in a certain parlor appointed and deputed to the same purpose, never without fire and clean water, nor yet without cradles, that when they will they may lay down the young infants, or at their pleasure take them out of their swathing clothes, and hold them to the fire, and refresh them with play. Every mother is nurse to her own child, unless either death or sickness prevent her. When that chances, the wives of the syphogrants quickly provide a nurse. And that is not hard to be done. For they that can do it, do offer themselves to no service so gladly as to that, because this kind of pity is much praised there, and the child that is nourished ever after takes his nurse for his own natural mother. Also among the nurses sit all the children that are under the age of five years. All the other children of both kinds, boys as well as girls, that are under the age of marriage, do either serve at the tables, or else if they are too young for that, stand by with marvelous silence. That which is given them from the table they eat, and a separate dinner-time they have none.

The syphogrant and his wife sit at the middle of the high table, forasmuch as that is counted the honorablest place, and because from thence all the whole company is in their sight. For that table stands across the upper end of the hall. To them are joined two of the ancientest and eldest. For at every table they sit four at a meal. But if there is a church in that syphogranty or ward, then the priest and his wife sit with the syphogrant, as chief of the company. On both sides of them sit young men, and next unto them again old men. And thus throughout all the house those of equal age are set together, and yet are mixed with unequal ages. This, they say, was ordained to the intent that the sage gravity and reverence of the elders should keep the younger from wanton license of words and behavior: forasmuch as nothing can be so secretly spoken or done at the table but that they who sit on the one side or on the other must needs perceive it. The dishes are not set down in order from the first place, but all the old men (whose places are marked with some special token to be known)

...e first served with their meat, and then the rest equally. The old men divide their dainties as they think best with the younger that sit on each side of them.

Thus the elders are not defrauded of their due honor, and nevertheless equal comfort comes to everyone. They begin every dinner and supper by reading something that pertains to good manners and virtue. But it is short, because no man shall be wearied thereby. Thereupon the elders take occasion for honest conversation, but neither sad nor unpleasant. Howbeit, they do not spend the whole dinner-time themselves in long and tedious talks, but they gladly hear also the young men; yea, and do purposely provoke them to talk, to the intent that they may have a proof of every man's wit, and inclination or disposition to virtue, which commonly in the liberty of feasting does show and utter itself.

Their dinners are very short, but their suppers are somewhat longer, because after dinner follows labor, after supper sleep and natural rest, which they think to be of more strength and efficacy to wholesome and healthful digestion. No supper goes by without music. Their banquets lack no dainties or delicacies. They burn sweet gums and spices for perfumes and pleasant smells, and sprinkle about sweet ointments and waters; yea, they leave nothing undone that makes for the cheering of the company. For they are much inclined to this opinion: to think no kind of pleasure forbidden wherefrom comes no harm. Thus therefore and after this sort they live together in the city, but in the country they that dwell alone far from any neighbors dine and sup at home in their own houses. For no family there lacks any kind of victuals, since from them comes all that the citizens eat and live by.

Of their journeying or traveling abroad, with divers other matters cleverly reasoned and wisely discussed

But if any are desirous to visit either their friends that dwell in another city, or to see the place itself, they easily obtain permission from their syphogrants and tranibores, unless there is some good reason. No man goes out alone, but a company is sent forth together with their prince's letters, which testify that they have permission to go that journey, and prescribes also the day of their return. They have a wagon given them, with a common bondman who drives the oxen and takes charge of them. But unless they have women in their company, they send home the wagon again, as an impediment and a hindrance. And though they carry nothing forth with them, yet in all their journey they lack for nothing. For wheresoever they come they are at home. If they tarry in a place longer than one day, then every one of them there takes up his own occupation, is very kindly treated by the workmen and companies of the same crafts. If any man on his own authority and without leave walks out of his precinct and bounds and is taken without the prince's letters, he is brought back as a fugitive or a runaway with great shame and rebuke, and is sharply punished. If he is taken in that fault again, he is punished with bondage.

If any be desirous to walk abroad into the fields, or into the country that belongs to the same city that he dwells in, and obtains the good will of his father, and the consent of his wife, he is not prohibited. But into whatever part of the country he comes he has no meat given him until he has worked out his forenoon's task, or else despatched as much work as is wont to be done there before supper. Observing this law and condition, he may go whither he will, within the bounds of his own city. For he will be no less profitable to the city than if he remained within it. Now you see how little liberty they have to loiter, how they can have no cloak or pretense for idleness. There are neither wine taverns, nor ale houses, nor brothels, nor any opportunity for vice or wickedness, no lurking corners, no places of wicked counsels or unlawful assemblies; but they are in full view and under the eyes of every man. So that of necessity they must either ply their accustomed labors or else refresh themselves with honest and laudable pastimes.

This being the practice of the people, they must of necessity have store and plenty of all things. And seeing they are all partners thereof equally, therefore no man can be poor there or needy. In the council of Amaurote, whither, as I said, every city sends three men apiece yearly, as soon as it is perfectly known of what things there is plenty in every place, and again of what there is scant store in any place, straightway the lack of one is supplied and filled up from the abundance of the other. And this they do freely without any benefit, taking nothing in return from them to whom the things are given; but those cities that have given of their store to another city that lacked, and demanded nothing again of the same city, take the things they lack from another city, to whom they gave nothing. So the whole island is, as it were, one family or household. But when they have made sufficient store of provision for themselves (which they think not done, until they have provided for the two years following, because of the uncertainty of the next year's crop) then from the things whereof they have abundance they carry forth into other countries great plenty, such as grain, honey, wool, flax, wood, madder, purple dye, skins, wax, tallow, leather, and living beasts. And one seventh of all these things they give frankly and freely to the poor of that country. The remainder they sell at a reasonable and moderate price.

By this trade or traffic of merchandise, they bring to their own country not only great plenty of gold and silver but also all such things as they lack at home, which is almost nothing but iron. And because they have long carried on this trade, now they have more abundance of these things than any man will believe. Now therefore they care not whether they sell for ready money, or else on trust to be paid at an appointed day, and so leave the most part in debts. But in so doing they never rely on the credit of private men, but on the assurance or guarantee of the whole city, by deeds and writings made to that effect accordingly. When the day of payment is come and expired, the city collects the debt from the private debtors, and puts it into the common box and has the use and profit of it until the Utopians, their creditors, demand it. The most part of it they never ask. For a thing which is to them no profit they do not take from others, to whom it is profitable; they think it not right nor fair.

But if it be the case that they must lend part of that money to another people, then they call in their debt; and when they have war. For that purpose only they gather at home all the treasure they have, to be helped and succored by it in extreme jeopardies, or in sudden dangers. But especially and chiefly to hire therewith, for unreasonable great wages, foreign soldiers. For they had rather put strangers in jeopardy than their own countrymen; they know, too, that for money enough their enemies themselves many times may be bought and sold, or else through treason set together by the ears among themselves. For this cause they keep an inestimable treasure. But yet not as treasure, but so they may have it, and use it, as in good faith I am ashamed to relate, fearing that my words shall not be believed. And this I have more cause to fear, for I know with what difficulty and hardly I myself would have believed another man telling the same, if I had not been present and seen it with mine own eyes.

For it must needs be, that in so far as a thing is alien and different from the manners and ways of the hearers, so far shall it be beyond their belief. Howbeit, a wise and impartial judge of things, seeing that all other laws and customs do so much differ from ours, will not greatly marvel perchance, if the use also of gold and silver among them is adapted rather to their own fashions than to ours. I mean in that they use no money themselves, but keep it for that chance, which either may happen, or may be, shall never come to pass. In the meantime, gold and silver, whereof money is made, they use as if none of them did esteem it more than the very nature of the thing deserved. And then who does not plainly see how far it is inferior to iron, without which men can no better live than without fire and water. Whereas to gold and silver nature has given no use that we may not well do without, if but the folly of men had not set it in high estimation for its rareness' sake. But on the other hand, nature as a most tender and loving mother has spread the best and most necessary things open abroad, as the air, the water, and the earth itself. And she has removed and hid farthest from us vain and unprofitable things.

Now if these metals among them were fast locked up in some tower, it might be suspected (as the people is ever foolishly imagining) that the prince and the council intended by some subtlety to deceive the commons, and to take some profit of them to themselves. Furthermore, if they made thereof plate and such other finely and cunningly wrought stuff, and if at any time they should have occasion to break it up and melt it again, and so therewith to pay their soldiers' wages, they see and perceive very well that men would be loath to part from those things that they had once begun to have pleasure and delight in. To remedy all this they have found a means, which, as it is agreeable to all their other laws and customs, so it is very different from ours, where gold is so much prized and so diligently kept, and is therefore incredible, except to them that are wise. For whereas they eat and drink in earthen and glass vessels, which are indeed elaborately and handsomely made, and yet of very small value, of gold and silver they commonly make chamber pots, and other like vessels that serve for most base uses, not only in their common halls, but in every man's private house. Furthermore, of the same metals they make the great chains with fetters and shackles wherein they bind their bondmen. Finally, whosoever for any offense is disgraced, in their ears they hang rings of gold, upon their fingers they wear rings of gold, and about their necks chains of gold, and, in conclusion, their heads are tied about with gold.

Thus by all means that may be they contrive to have gold and silver among them held in reproach and infamy. And therefore these metals, which other nations do as grievously and sorrowfully give up, as in a manner from their own lives, if they should altogether be taken at once from the Utopians, no man there would think he had lost the worth of one farthing. They gather also pearls by the seaside, and diamonds and carbuncles upon certain rocks; and yet they seek not for them, but when by chance they find them, they cut and polish them. And therewith they deck their young infants, who in the first years of their childhood make much of and are fond and proud of such ornaments, but when they are a little more grown in years and discretion, perceiving that none but children do wear such toys and trifles, they lay them away even of their own shamefacedness, without any bidding of their parents, even as our children, when they grow big, cast away nuts, trinkets, and dolls. What different fancies and tastes these laws and customs, which are so far unlike those of all other nations, do create I never perceived so plainly as in the case of the Anemolians.

These ambassadors came to Amaurote while I was there. And because they came to treat of great and weighty matters, the three citizens from every city were come thither before them. But all the ambassadors of the neighboring countries who had been there before and knew the fashions and manners of the Utopians, by whom they had seen no honor given to sumptuous and costly apparel, silks condemned, gold despised and disreputable, were wont to come thither in very homely and simple apparel. But the Anemolians, because they dwell far thence and had very little acquaintance with them, hearing that they were all clothed alike, and that very rudely and homely, thinking they did not have the things which they did not wear and being therefore more proud than wise, determined in the gorgeousness of their apparel to represent the very gods, and with the bright shining and glittering of their gay clothing to dazzle the eyes of the simple Utopians. So there arrived three ambassadors with one hundred servants all appareled in changeable colors, most of them in silks, the ambassadors themselves (for at home in their own country they were noblemen) in cloth of gold, with great chains of gold, gold hanging at their ears, gold rings upon their fingers, brooches and pendants of gold upon their caps, which glittered full of pearls and precious stones; in brief, trimmed and adorned with all those things, which among the Utopians were either the punishment of bondmen, or the reproach of disgraced persons, or else trifles for young children to play with. Thereat it would have done a man good at his heart to see how proudly they displayed their peacock's feathers, how much they made of their painted sheaths, and how loftily they set out and displayed themselves, when they compared their gallant apparel with the poor raiment of the Utopians. For all the people swarmed forth into the streets. And on the other side it was no less pleasure to consider how much they were being deceived, and how far they missed of their purpose, being contrariwise regarded to what they thought they were.

For to the eyes of all the Utopians, except a very few, who had been in other countries for some reasonable cause, all that gorgeousness of apparel seemed shameful and reproachful. Insomuch that they most reverently saluted the basest and most abject of them for lords, passing over the ambassadors themselves without any honor, judging them by their wearing of golden chains to be the bondmen. Yea, you should have seen the children also who had cast away their pearls and precious stones, when they saw the like stuck on the ambassadors' caps, dig and push their mothers under their sides, saying to them: "Look, mother, how great a lubber still wears pearls and precious stones, as though he were a little child still." But the mother, yea, and that also in good earnest: "Peace, son," says she. "I think he is one of the ambassadors' fools." Some found fault with their golden chains, as of no use or purpose, being so thin and weak that a bondman might easily break them, or else so wide and loose that when it pleased him he might pull them off, and run away at liberty whither he would. But when the ambassadors had been there a day or two and saw so great abundance of gold so lightly esteemed, yea, in as much reproach as it was with them in honor; and, besides that, more gold in the chains and shackles of one fugitive bondman than all the costly ornaments of the three were worth, they began to lose their spirits, and for very shame laid away all that gorgeous array whereof they had been so proud. And especially when they had talked familiarly with the Utopians, and had learned all their fashions and opinions.

For these marvel that any man is so foolish as to find delight and pleasure in the glittering of a little trifling stone, who may behold any of the stars, or else the sun itself. Or that any man is so mad as to count himself the nobler for the smaller or finer thread of wool; which selfsame wool—be it now never so fine spun a thread—did a sheep once wear, and yet was she all that time no other thing than a sheep. They marvel also that gold, which of its own nature is a thing so unprofitable, is now among all people in such high estimation that man himself, by whom, yea and for the use of whom it is so much valued, is in much less estimation than the gold. Insomuch that a lumpish, blockheaded churl, who has no more wit than an ass, yea, and is as full of worthlessness and foolishness, shall hold nevertheless many wise and good men in subjection and bondage, only for this, because he owns a great heap of gold. Which if it should be taken from him by any fortune, or by some subtle wile of the law, which no less than fortune raises up the low and plucks down the high, and be given to the most vile slave and abject drudge of all his household, then shortly after he would go into the service of his servant, as an augmentation or an overplus beside his money.[14] But much more do they marvel at and detest the madness of those who give to those rich men, in whose debt and power they are not, but because they are rich; although they know them to be such niggardly skinflints that they are sure that as long as they live not one farthing's worth of that heap of gold shall come to them.

These and such like opinions have they conceived, partly through education, being brought up in that commonwealth, whose laws and customs are far different from these kinds of folly, and partly through good literature and learning. For though there are not many in every city who are exempt and discharged from all other labors, and appointed only to learning; that is to say, in whom even from their very childhood they have perceived a singular forwardness, a fine wit, and a mind apt to good learning; yet all, in their childhood, are instructed in learning. And the better part of the people, both men and women, throughout all their whole life do bestow on learning those spare hours, which we said they have free from bodily labors. They are taught learning in their own native tongue. For it is both copious in words, and also pleasant to the ear, and for the utterance of a man's thought very perfect and sure. Almost all of that side of the world uses

[14] This belittling of gold and silver and material wealth is a feature of Plato's ideal commonwealth (*The Republic,* III, Classics Club edition, p. 305), and also appears in Francis Bacon's *The New Atlantis* (Classics Club edition, p. 273). Amerigo Vespucci reported that native tribes visited in his fourth voyage cared nothing for pearls, jewels, and gold.

the same language, save that among the Utopians it is finest and purest; and according to the diversity of the countries it is diversely altered.

Of all those philosophers whose names are here famous in this part of the world, not so much as the fame of one of them was come among the Utopians before our going thither. And yet in music, logic, arithmetic, and geometry they have discovered in their manner all that our ancient philosophers have taught. But whereas they in all things are almost equal to our old ancient scholars, our new logicians have far passed and gone beyond them in subtle inventions. For they have devised not one of all those rules of restrictions, amplifications, and suppositions, very wittily invented in the small logicals, which here our children in every place do learn. Furthermore, they were never yet able to find out the second intentions; insomuch that none of them all could ever see man himself in common, as they call him, though he is, as you know, bigger than ever was any giant, yea and pointed to by us even with our finger.[15] But in the courses of the stars and the movings

15 In this and the above sentence More ridicules what he regards as the barren subtleties of the scholastic philosophers who had dominated English and European universities since the Middle Ages. The "second intention" and the "first intention" were terms used to define certain of their concepts. Their teachings were equally decried by practically all Renaissance scholars. Butler in his *Hudibras* describes one of their number in this fashion:

> He was in Logic a great critic,
> Profoundly skill'd in Analytic
> He could distinguish and divide;
> A hair twixt south and southwest side.
> (Part I, Canto 1.)

of the heavenly spheres they are very expert and cunning. They have also wisely excogitated and devised instruments of divers fashions, wherein are exactly included and contained the movings and situations of the sun, the moon, and all the other stars which appear in their horizon. But as for the alliances and dissensions of the planets, and all that deceitful divination by the stars, they never as much as dreamed thereof.[16] Rains, winds, and the courses of tempests they predict by certain tokens, which they have learned by long use and observation. But as to the causes of all these things and of the ebbing, flowing, and saltness of the sea, and, finally, of the original beginning and nature of heaven and the world, they hold partly the same opinions that our old philosophers held, and partly, as our philosophers vary among themselves, so they also at times propose new reasons for things, and disagree from all of them, and yet among themselves on all points do not accord.

In that division of philosophy which treats of manners and virtue, their reasons and opinions agree with ours. They discuss the good qualities of the soul, of the body, and of fortune, and whether the name goodness may be applied to all these, or only to the endowments and gifts of the soul. They reason of virtue and pleasure. But their chief and principal question is in what thing, be it one or more, does the felicity of

16 It is interesting that More has the Utopians distinguish between astronomy and astrology, and to look with disdain on the latter. For astrologers were still patronized by members of all classes in More's day and even great Renaissance astronomers, like Tycho Brahe and Kepler, had not completely discarded astrology.

man consist.[17] On this point they seem almost too much given and inclined to the opinion of those who defend pleasure, in which they say either all or the chief part of man's felicity rests. And (which is more to be marveled at) the defense of this so dainty and soft an opinion they derive even from their grave, austere, sober, and rigorous religion. For they never discuss felicity or blessedness without joining to the reasons of philosophy certain principles taken from religion; without which for the investigation of true felicity they think reason alone weak and imperfect. Those principles are these and such like: that the soul is immortal, and by the bountiful goodness of God ordained to felicity; that for our virtues and good deeds rewards are appointed after this life, and for our evil deeds, punishments.

Though these ideas belong to religion, yet they think it right they should be believed and confirmed by proofs of reason. But if these principles should be condemned and annulled, then without any delay they would pronounce no man so foolish as not to put forth all his diligence and endeavor to obtain pleasure by right or wrong, avoiding only this error, that the less pleasure should be a hindrance to a bigger, or that he should labor for a pleasure which would bring after it displeasure, grief, and sorrow. For they judge it extreme madness to follow a sharp and painful virtue, and not only to

17 In the succeeding paragraphs More has given the Utopians a moral philosophy that is something of a mixture of Christian ethics, Epicureanism, and Stoicism. Here not Plato but Cicero, in his discourse *About the Ends of Goods and Evils*, appears to be More's guide in respect to the two pagan schools of thought.

banish the pleasure of life, but also of one's own accord to suffer grief without any hope of profit therefrom. For what profit can there be, if a man, when he has spent all his life unpleasantly, that is to say, wretchedly, has no reward after his death?

But now, sir, they do not think felicity is in all pleasure, but only in that pleasure that is good and honest, and that to it, as to perfect blessedness, our nature is allured and drawn even by virtue, to which alone they that are of the contrary opinion attribute felicity. For they define virtue as a life ordered according to nature, and say that we are hereunto ordained by God; and that a man follows the course of nature, when in desiring and refusing things he is ruled by reason. Furthermore, that reason does firstly and principally kindle in men the love and veneration of the divine majesty, of whose goodness it is that we are, and that we are able to attain felicity. And that, secondly, it moves and encourages us to lead our life free of care in joy and mirth, and to help all others in the fellowship of nature to obtain the same. For there was never a man so earnest and painstaking a follower of virtue and hater of pleasure, who would so enjoin you to labors, watchings, and fastings, but he would also exhort you to ease, and lighten, to your power, the poverty and misery of others, praising the same as a deed of humanity and pity.

Then if it be a point of humanity for man to bring health and comfort to man, and especially (which is a virtue most peculiarly belonging to man) to mitigate and assuage the grief of others, and by taking from them the sorrow and heaviness of life, to restore them to joy, that is to say, to pleasure, why may it not then be said that nature incites every man to do the same for himself? For a joyful life, that is to say, a pleasant life, is either evil, and if it be so, then thou should not only help no man win it, but rather, as much as in thee lies, help all men to shun it, as troublous and hurtful; or else, if thou not only may, but also are bound of duty to procure it for others, why not then chiefly for thyself, to whom thou art bound to show as much favor as to others? For when nature bids thee to be good and gentle to others she commands thee not to be cruel and ungentle to thyself. Therefore even nature herself, say they, prescribes to us a joyful life, that is to say, pleasure as the end of all our operations. And they define virtue as life ordered according to the law of nature. Nature does also allure and incite men to help one another to live merrily, which surely she does not without good cause, for no man is so far above the lot of man's state or condition that nature cares for him only, but she equally favors all comprehended in the communion of one shape, form, and fashion. So verily she commands thee to use diligent circumspection not so to seek for thine own comfort as to procure for others discomfort.

Wherefore the Utopians' opinion is that not only covenants and bargains made between private men ought to be well and faithfully fulfilled, observed, and kept; but also common laws, which either a good prince has justly published, or else the people, neither oppressed with tyranny nor deceived by fraud and guile, have by their common consent constituted and ratified, concerning the partition of the comfort of life, that is to say, the materials of pleasure. As long as these laws are not violated it is wisdom that thou look to thine own wealth. And to do the same for the commonwealth is no less than thy duty, if thou bear any reverent love or any natural zeal and affection to thy native country. But to go about to keep another man from his pleasure, whilst thou procure thine own, that is open wrong. Contrariwise, to deprive thyself of something to give to another, that is a mark of humanity and gentleness, which never takes away so much comfort as it brings again. For it is recompensed by the return of benefits; and the consciousness of the good deed, with the remembrance of the thankful love and benevolence of those to whom thou hast done it, brings more pleasure to thy mind than that which thou hast withheld from thyself could have brought to thy body. Finally (and of this a godly-disposed and religious mind is easy to persuade) God recompenses the gift of a short and small pleasure with great and everlasting joy.

Therefore, having diligently weighed and considered the matter, they think that all our actions, and with them the virtues themselves are to be referred at the last to pleasure as their end, and to felicity. Pleasure they call every motion and state of the body or mind wherein man naturally feels delectation. Appetite they link with nature, and that not without good cause. For as not only the senses but also right reason covets whatsoever is naturally pleasant, as long as it is gotten without wrong or injury, and without hindering or debarring a greater pleasure, or causing painful labor, even so those things against nature that men by vain imagination feign are pleasant (as though it lay in their power to change things, as they do the names of things) —all such pleasures they believe to be of such small help and furtherance to felicity that they count them great trouble and hindrance. Because in whatever man they have once become firmly rooted, they possess all his mind with a false opinion of pleasure, so that there is no place left in him for true and natural delights.

For there are many things, which of their own nature contain no pleasantness; yea, the most of them much grief and sorrow, and yet through the perverse and malicious, flickering enticements of lewd and dishonorable desires, they are taken not only for special and sovereign pleasures, but also are counted among the chief causes of life. Among this counterfeit kind of pleasures they put those that I spoke of before; when the better gown they have on, the better men they think themselves. In which thing they do doubly err; for they are no less deceived in that they think their gown better than they are in that they think themselves better. For if you consider the profitable use of the garment, why should wool of a fine-spun thread be thought better than the wool of a coarse-spun thread? Yet they, as though the one did surpass the other by nature, and not by their own mistake, exalt themselves, and think the worth of their own persons greatly increased. And therefore the honor, which in a coarse gown they dared not have looked for, they demand, as if it were a duty, for their finer gown's sake. And if they are passed by without reverence, they take it angrily and disdainfully.

Again, is it not like madness to take pride in vain and unprofitable honors? For what natural or true pleasure dost thou take in another man's bare head, or bowed knees? Will that ease the pain of thy knees, or remedy the frenzy of thy head? In following this image of counterfeit pleasure, they are of marvelous madness who think themselves of noble birth, rejoice much in their conceit, because it was their fortune to come of ancestors whose stock of long time has been counted rich (for now nobility is nothing else)—especially rich in lands. And though their ancestors left them not one foot of land, yet they think themselves not a hair's breadth the less noble. In this number also are counted those who take pleasure and delight, as I said, in gems and precious stones, and think themselves almost gods if they chance to get an excellent one, especially of that kind which at that time is held by their own countrymen in highest estimation. For no one kind of stone keeps its price constant in all countries and at all times. And they buy them not unless they are taken out of the gold and are bare: and not either before they have made the seller swear that he will warrant and assure it to be a true stone and no counterfeit gem. Such care they take lest a counterfeit stone should deceive their eyes instead of a right stone. But why shouldst thou not take as much pleasure in beholding a counterfeit stone, which thine eye cannot distinguish from a right stone? They should both be of like value to thee, even as to a blind man.

What shall I say of those who keep superfluous riches, to take delight in the beholding only, and not in the use or employment thereof? Do they take true pleasure, or are they deceived with false pleasure? Or of those who go to the other extreme, hiding the gold which they shall never use, or peradventure never see more; and while they take care lest they lose it, lose it indeed? For what else is it, when they hide it in the ground, taking it both from their own use, and perchance from all other men's also? And yet thou, when thou hast hid thy treasure, as one free of all care, dancest for joy. Which treasure, if it should chance to be stolen, and thou, still ignorant of the theft, should die ten years after, all that ten years' space that thou did live after thy money was stolen, what matter was it to thee, whether it had been taken away from thee or else was safe as thou left it? Truly, both ways the same profit came to thee.

To these so foolish pleasures the Utopians join dicers, whose madness they know by hearsay and not by experience; hunters also and hawkers. For what pleasure is there, they say, in casting the dice on a table, which thou hast done so often, that if there were any pleasure in it, yet the frequent repetition might make thee weary of it? Or what delight can there be, and not rather annoyance, in hearing the barking and howling of dogs? Or what greater pleasure is there to be felt when a dog follows a hare than when a dog follows a dog? For the same thing is done in both, that is to say, running,—if thou hast pleasure in that. But if the hope of slaughter and the expectation of tearing the beast in pieces please thee, thou shouldst rather be moved by pity to see a silly innocent hare murdered by a dog, the weak by the stronger, the fearful by the fierce, the innocent by the cruel and unmerciful. Therefore all this exercise of hunting, as a thing unworthy to be a practice of free men, the Utopians have relegated to their butchers, to which craft, as we said before, they appoint their bondmen. For they count hunting the lowest, the vilest, the most abject part of butchery, and the other parts of it more profitable and more honest, which produce goods much more useful, and kill beasts only for necessity. Whereas the hunter seeks nothing but pleasure from the silly and woeful beasts' slaughter and murder. And this pleasure in beholding death they think gives rise in the very beasts, either to a cruel turn of mind, or else is changed in course of time into cruelty, by long habit of so cruel a pleasure.[18]

These, therefore, and all such like, which are innumerable, though the common sort of people take them for pleasures, yet the Utopians, seeing there is no natural pleasantness in them, plainly declare they have no affinity with true and right pleasure. For even though they do commonly move the senses with delight (which seems to be a work of pleasure), this does nothing to weaken their opinion. For not the nature of the thing, but men's perverse and lewd custom is the reason which causes them to accept bitter or sour things as sweet; even as women with child in their vitiated and corrupt taste think pitch and tallow sweeter than any honey. Howbeit, no man's judgment, depraved and corrupted either by sickness or by custom, can change the nature of pleasure more than it can the nature of other things.

The Utopians count divers kinds of true pleasures. Some

[18] An aversion to hunting as a sport and a conviction that cruelty to animals has ill effects on the finer nature of man are to be found in the writings of various classical authors. It is an attitude particularly associated with the Greek philosopher Pythagoras.

they attribute to the soul, and some to the body. To the soul they give intelligence and that delight that comes from the contemplation of truth. Hereunto is joined the pleasant remembrance of a good life past and the promise of future happiness. The pleasure of the body they divide into two parts. The first is when delight is felt and perceived by the senses. . . . The second part of bodily pleasure, they say, is that which consists and rests in the quiet and harmonious state of the body. And that truly is every man's own proper health, intermingled and disturbed with no pain. For this, if it be not hampered or assaulted with pain, is delectable in itself, though it be caused by no external or outward pleasure. For though it is not so plain and manifest to the senses as the greedy lusts of eating and drinking, yet nevertheless many take it for the chiefest pleasure. All the Utopians grant it to be a right great pleasure, and, as you would say, the foundation and ground of all pleasures, which even alone is able to make the state and condition of life delectable and pleasant. And it being once lost, there is no place left for any pleasure. For mere freedom from pain without real health, they call insensibility, and not pleasure.

The Utopians have long ago rejected and condemned the opinion of those who said that steadfast and quiet health (for this question also has been diligently debated among them) ought not therefore to be counted a pleasure, because, they say, it cannot be presently and sensibly perceived by the senses and felt in some outward motion. On the contrary, they now agree almost all in this, that health is a sovereign pleasure. For seeing that in sickness, say they, is pain, which is a mortal enemy to pleasure, even as sickness is to health, why then should there not be pleasure in the quietness of health? For they say it makes no difference whether you say that sickness is a pain, or that in sickness is pain, for it all means the same. For whether health is a pleasure itself, or a necessary cause of pleasure, as fire is of heat, truly both ways it follows that they cannot be without pleasure that are in perfect health. Furthermore, while we eat, say they, then health, which was beginning to be impaired, fights with the help of food against hunger; in which fight, while health little by little gets the upper hand, that proceeding, and—as you would say—that advance toward our wonted strength, which thing only it desired in all the fight, shall it be astonished? Shall it not know or embrace its own wealth or goodness? For though it is said health cannot be felt, this they think is not true. For what man waking, say they, does not feel himself in health, but he that is not? Is there any man so possessed by stony insensibility, or by the sleeping sickness, that he will not acknowledge that health is acceptable to him, and delectable? And what else is delectation, but that which by another name is called pleasure?

The Utopians cultivate chiefly the pleasures of the mind. For those they count the chiefest and most principal of all. The greater part of them they think come from the exercise of virtue and the consciousness of a good life. Of the pleasures that the body provides, they give pre-eminence to health. For the delights of eating and drinking and whatever has like pleasantness, they describe as pleasures much to be desired, but in no other way than for health's sake. For such things by their own proper nature are not pleasant, but only as they resist a sickness secretly stealing on. Therefore as it is a wise man's part rather to avoid sickness than to wish for medicines, and rather to drive away and put to flight the pains which bring care and worry than to call for comfort; so it is much better not to need this kind of pleasure than to be curing with it the contrary pain in order to be eased of the same. Which kind of pleasure, if any man choose for his felicity, that man must needs grant that then his felicity shall be greater, if he live a life of continual hunger, thirst, itching, eating, drinking, scratching, and rubbing. Which life, who perceives not how not only foul it is, but also how miserable and wretched? These doubtless are the basest pleasures of all, both impure and imperfect. For they never come but accompanied by their contrary pains; since to the pleasure of eating is joined hunger, and after that no very equal sort. For of these two the pain is both the more vehement, and also of longer continuance. It rises before the pleasure, and ends not until the pleasure dies with it. Wherefore such pleasures the Utopians think are not greatly to be prized, but in so far as they are necessary. Howbeit, they enjoy them too, and thankfully acknowledge the tender love of mother nature, who with most pleasant delight allures her children to that which of necessity they are driven often to use. For how wretched and miserable should our life be, if these daily pangs of hunger and thirst could not be driven away but with bitter potions and sour medicines, as other diseases are, wherewith we are seldom troubled!

Beauty, strength, nimbleness—these as peculiar and pleasant gifts of nature they make much of. And those pleasures which are received by the ears, the eyes, and the nose, which nature wills to be proper and peculiar to man (for no other kind of living beast beholds the fairness and the beauty of the world, or is moved by any regard for savors but only for the diversity of meats, or perceives the concordant and discordant intervals of sounds and tunes)—these pleasures, I say, they accept and approve as certain pleasant rejoicings of life. But in all things they take this precaution, that a less pleasure shall not hinder a bigger, and that a pleasure be no cause of displeasure, which they think will follow of necessity, if the pleasure be dishonorable. But to despise the comeliness of beauty, to waste bodily strength, to turn nimbleness into sluggishness, to consume and make feeble the body with fasting, to do injury to health, and to reject the other pleasant gifts of nature—unless a man neglect these his comforts only, while with a fervent zeal he is procuring the wealth of others or the common profit, for which pleasures refused he is in hope of a greater pleasure at God's hand—otherwise for a vain shadow of virtue, for no man's wealth and profit, to punish himself, or hope thereby to be able courageously to suffer adversities, which perchance shall never come to him; to do this they think a mark of extreme madness, and a token of a man cruelly minded toward himself, and unkind toward nature, as so disdaining to be in her power that he renounces and refuses all her benefits.

This is the Utopians' judgment and opinion of virtue and pleasure. And they believe that none can be found by man's reason truer than this, unless some godlier inspiration comes to man from heaven. Wherein, whether they believe well or not, neither does time suffer us to discuss, nor is it now necessary. For we have taken upon us to describe and declare their opinions and ordinances, and not to defend them. But this thing, I verily believe, however these decrees may be, there is in no place in the world either a more excellent people or a more flourishing commonwealth. They are light and quick of body, full of activity and nimbleness, and of more strength than a man would judge by their stature, which for all that is not too low. And though their soil is not very fruitful, nor their air very wholesome, yet against the air they so defend themselves with temperate diet, and so order and till their ground with diligent labor that in no country is greater increase or plenty of corn and cattle, or men's bodies of longer life and subject or liable to fewer diseases. There, therefore, a man may see well and diligently performed and carried out not only those things which farmers do commonly in other countries by craft and cunning to remedy the barrenness of the ground, but also a whole wood by the hands of the people plucked up by the roots in one place, and set out again in another place. Wherein they had regard and consideration, not for a greater supply but for more convenient transport, that wood and timber might be nigher to the sea or the rivers or the cities. For it is less labor and effort to carry grain far by land than wood.

The people are gentle, merry, quick, and fine-witted, delighting in leisure, but when need requires able to endure and suffer much bodily labor. Otherwise they are not greatly desirous or fond of it; but in the exercise and study of the mind they are never weary. When they had heard me speak of Greek literature or learning (for in Latin there was nothing that I thought they would greatly admire, besides the historians and the poets) they made wonderfully earnest and importunate entreaties to me that I would teach and instruct them in that tongue and learning. I began therefore to read to them, at first, truly, more because I would not seem to refuse the labor than that I hoped that they would anything profit thereby. But when I had gone forward a little, I soon perceived by their diligence that my labor should not be bestowed in vain; for they began so easily to fashion the letters, so plainly to pronounce the words, so quickly to learn by heart, and so surely to repeat the same, that I marveled at it, save that most of them were fine and chosen wits, of ripe age, picked out of the company of learned men, who not only of their own free and voluntary will, but also by the command of the council, undertook to learn this language. Therefore in less than three years' space there was nothing in the Greek tongue that they did not have. They were able to read good authors without any stumbling, if the text were not at fault.

This kind of learning, I suppose, they took to much the sooner, because it is somewhat allied to them. For I think that this nation took its beginning from the Greeks, because their speech, which in all other points is not much unlike the Persian tongue, keeps divers signs and tokens of the Greek language in the names of their cities and of their magistrates. They have from me (for when I determined to undertake my fourth voyage, I stowed in the ship instead of merchandise a bundle of books, because I intended never to return, or not for a long time) the

most of Plato's works, more of Aristotle's, also Theophrastus
on plants, though, in divers places, which I am sorry for, imperfect. For while we were sailing, a marmoset chanced upon
the book, as it was negligently laid by, and wantonly playing
therewith plucked out certain leaves and tore them in pieces.
Of authors who have written on grammar, they have only
Lascaris.[19] For Theodorus I carried not with me, nor ever a
dictionary but Hesychius and Dioscorides.[20] They set great
store by Plutarch's books. And they are delighted with Lucian's
merry conceits and jests. Of the poets they have Aristophanes,
Homer, Euripides, and Sophocles in Aldus' small print.[21] Of

---

[19] Constantine Lascaris was one of the Greek scholars who took refuge in Italy
after the fall of Constantinople in 1453, and there did much to promote the
revival of Greek learning. His *Grammar* is thought to be the first book entirely
in Greek to come from the newly invented printing press.

[20] Theodorus Gaza was another Greek refugee who came to Italy in the fifteenth
century and aided in the revival of classical knowledge. His Greek grammar was
printed by the Aldine press in 1495. Hesychius, a native of Alexandria, was
probably born in the fifth century. His Greek dictionary, published by the Aldine
press in 1514, was noted for its copious lists of strange and unusual words,
many of them from little known Greek dialects. Pedanius Dioscorides was a
Cilician of the first or second century, whose celebrated work on medicinal sub-
stances and their properties was printed for the first time in 1499 by the Aldine
press.

[21] This list is in itself a commentary on the work of the Aldine press. Aldus
Manutius, founder of the famous printing establishment, was born in Italy in
1450. As a young man, he studied Greek under some of the best Renaissance
masters and became possessed with the ambition to put the best of all that
remained of Greek literature, as yet mostly in manuscript, into printed form.
He set up his press at Venice, where a large group of Greek scholars became
associated with him. Latin and Italian as well as Greek works were printed. His
goal was to print books that would be beautiful, accurate, and within the
reach of people of moderate means. To a remarkable degree, he realized all
three of these aims.

ıne historians they have Thucydides, Herodotus, and Herodian.[22] Also my companion, Tricius Apinatus, carried with him
medical books, certain small works of Hippocrates and Galen's
Microtechne.[23] The last book they hold in great esteem. For
though there is almost no nation under heaven that has less
need of medicine than they, yet this notwithstanding, medicine
is nowhere in greater honor; because they count the knowledge
of it among the goodliest and most profitable parts of philosophy.
For while by the help of philosophy they search out the secret
mysteries of nature, they think that they not only receive thereby
wonderful great pleasure, but also obtain great thanks and
favor from the author and maker thereof. For he, they think,
according to the fashion of other artificers, has set forth the
marvelous and gorgeous frame of the world for man to behold,
who alone has the wit and capacity to consider and understand
the excellence of so great a work. And therefore, they say, he
bears more good will and love to the careful and diligent be-
holder and viewer of his work and marveler at the same, than
he does to him, who like a very beast without wit and reason,
or as one without sense or motion, pays no regard to so great
and wonderful a spectacle. The wits also of the Utopians, inured
and exercised in learning, are marvelously quick in the invention of ways to help any toward the advantage and wealth of
life.

[22] Herodian was a Greek of the third century who wrote a history of his own
ʾimes.
[23] The *Microtechne* of Galen was a small work as distinct from his *Megalo·
techne.* a fuller and more complete medical treatise.

Howbeit two skills they may thank us for. That is, the science of printing, and the craft of making paper. And yet not only us, but chiefly and principally themselves. For when we showed them the print of Aldus in books of paper, and told them of the stuff whereof paper is made, and of the art of engraving letters, saying somewhat more than we actually knew, for there was none of us that knew perfectly either the one or the other, they forthwith very cleverly conjectured how it was. And whereas before they wrote only on skins, on barks of trees, and on reeds, now they have attempted to make paper, and to print letters. And though at first it proved not all of the best, yet by often trying the same they shortly got the knack of doing both, and have so far succeeded that if they had copies of the Greek authors, they would lack no books. But now they have no more than those I named before, save that by printing of the books they have multiplied and increased the same into many thousands of copies. Whosoever comes thither to see the land, and is excellent in any gift of wit, or through much long journeying is experienced and well versed in the knowledge of many countries (for which cause we were very welcome to them) they receive and entertain most kindly and lovingly. For they delight to hear what is done in every land; howbeit, very few merchantmen come thither, for what should they bring thither, unless it were iron, or gold and silver, which they had rather carry home again? Also such things as are to be carried out of their land, they think it more wise to carry those goods forth themselves, than that others should come thither to fetch them, to the intent they may the better know the foreign lands on every side of them, and keep in practice the art and knowledge of sailing.

Of bondmen, sick persons, wedlock, and divers other matters

They neither make bondmen of prisoners taken in battle, unless it is in a battle they fought themselves, nor of bondmen's children, nor, to be brief, of any man whom they can get out of another country, even though he were there a bondman. But they take either such as among themselves for heinous offenses are punished with bondage, or else such as in the cities of other lands are condemned to death for great trespasses. And of this sort of bondmen they have most store.

Many of them they bring home, sometimes paying very little for them, yea most commonly getting them gratis. These sorts of bondmen they keep not only in continual work and labor, but also in bonds. But their own men they handle hardest, for they judge them more desperate, and deserving of greater punishment, because after being so godly brought up to virtue in so excellent a commonwealth, they could not for all that be restrained from misdoing. Another kind of bondman they have: when a vile drudge, being a poor laborer in another country, chooses of his own free will to be a bondman among them. These they handle and order justly, and treat almost as kindly as their own free citizens, save that they put them to a little more labor, as being accustomed thereto. If any such is disposed to depart thence, which is seldom seen, they neither hold him against his will nor send him away with empty hands.

The sick, as I said, they see to with great affection, and omit nothing at all in the way of either medicine or good diet whereby they may be restored again to their health. Those that are sick of incurable diseases they comfort with sitting by them, talking with them, and, in brief, with all manner of helps that are at hand. But if the disease is not only incurable, but also full of continual pain and anguish, then the priests and the magistrates exhort the man, seeing he is not able to perform any duty of life, and by outliving his own death is harmful and irksome to others and grievous to himself, that he will determine with himself to cherish no longer that pestilent and painful disease. And seeing his life is to him but a torment, that he be not unwilling to die, but rather take to himself good hope, and either despatch himself out of this painful life, as out of a prison or a rack of torment, or else suffer himself willingly to be rid of it by others. And in so doing they tell him he will do wisely, seeing that by his death he shall lose no comfort, but end his pain. And because in that act he will follow the counsel of the priests, that is to say, of the interpreters of God's will and pleasure, they show him that he will be acting like a godly and virtuous man. They that are thus persuaded, finish their lives willingly, either by hunger, or else die in their sleep without any feeling of death. And they cause none such to die against his will, nor do they use less diligence and attendance about him, believing this to be an honorable death. On the contrary, he that kills himself before the priests and the council have sanctioned the cause of his death, him they cast unburied into some stinking marsh, as unworthy both of the earth and of fire.

A woman is not married before she is eighteen years old.[24] The man is four years older before he marries. If either a man or a woman is proved to have bodily offended before marriage with another, he or she—whichever it be—is sharply punished. And both the offenders are forbidden ever after in all their life to marry, unless the fault is forgiven by the prince's pardon. But both the master and the mistress of the house where that offense was committed are in danger of great reproach and infamy, as being slack and negligent in looking to their charges. That offense is so sharply punished, because they perceive that unless the people are diligently kept from the liberty of this vice, few will join together in the love of marriage, wherein all the life must be led with one, and also all the griefs and displeasures that come therewith must be patiently taken and borne. Furthermore, in choosing wives and husbands they observe earnestly and strictly a custom which seemed to us very silly and foolish. For a grave and honest matron shows the woman, be she maid or widow, naked to the wooer. And likewise a sage and discreet man exhibits the wooer naked to the woman. At this custom we laughed and disapproved it as foolish. But they on the other hand wonder greatly at the folly of all other nations, which in buying a colt, where a little money is

[24] Both the common law and the civil law in More's England designated twelve years as the minimum marriage age for a girl and fourteen for a boy; but contemporary writers on social and ethical questions were of the opinion that each should be older.

at stake, are so chary and circumspect, that though he be almost all bare, yet they will not buy him unless the saddle and all the harness are taken off, lest under those coverings is hid some gall or sore. And yet in choosing a wife, who shall be either pleasure or trouble to them all their life after, they are so reckless that while all the rest of the woman's body is covered with clothes, they judge her by scarcely one hand-breadth (for they can see no more than her face), and so join her to them not without great peril of evil agreeing together, if anything in her body afterward offend and displease them.

For all men are not so wise as to base their regard on the virtuous condition of the party. And the endowments of the body cause the virtues of the mind to be less esteemed and regarded; yea, even in the marriages of wise men. Verily, so foul a deformity may be hid under those coverings that it may quite alienate a man's mind from his wife, when it may not be lawful for their bodies to be separate again. If such a deformity happen by any chance to occur after the marriage is consummated and finished, well, there is no remedy but patience. Every man must take his fortune, alas! But it were well that a law were made whereby all such deceits might be prevented and avoided beforehand. And this they were constrained more earnestly to consider, because they only of the nations in that part of the world are content every man with one wife apiece.

And matrimony is there never broken, but by death; unless adultery break the bond, or else the intolerable, wayward habits of either party. If either of them find themselves for any such cause aggrieved, they may by the license of the council change and take another. But the other party lives ever after in infamy and out of wedlock. But for a husband to put away his wife for no fault but that some mishap is fallen to her body, this by no means will they permit. For they judge it a great mark of cruelty that anybody in their most need of help and comfort should be cast off and forsaken, and that old age, which both brings sickness with it and is a sickness itself, should be unkindly and unfaithfully dealt with. But now and then it chances that although a man and a woman cannot well agree between themselves, they both of them find others with whom they hope to live more quietly and merrily, and they with the full consent of them both are divorced asunder and new married to others. But that is not without the authority of the council, which agrees to no divorces, before they and their wives have diligently heard and examined the matter. Yea, and even then also they are loath to consent to it, because they know this is the quickest way to break love between man and wife, to be in easy hope of a new marriage. Breakers of wedlock are punished with most grievous bondage. And if both the offenders were married, then the parties which in that case have suffered wrong, are divorced from the adulterers, if they will, and married together, or else to whomever they like. But if either of them still continues to love so unkind a bedfellow, the habit of wedlock is not to them forbidden, if the party is disposed to follow in toiling and drudgery the person who for the offense is condemned to bondage. And very oft it chances that the repentance of the one, and the earnest industry of the other, so moves the prince with pity and compassion, that he restores the bond person from servitude to liberty and freedom again. But if the same party is taken again in fault, there is no other way but death.

To other trespassers there is no prescribed punishment appointed by any law. But according to the heinousness of the offense or the contrary, so the punishment is moderated by the discretion of the council. The husbands chastise their wives,[25] and the parents their children, unless they have committed so horrible an offense that the public punishment thereof does much to promote the advancement of honest manners. But most commonly the most heinous faults are punished with the hardship of bondage. For this they suppose is to the offenders no less painful and to the commonwealth more profitable than if they hastily put them to death, and removed them out of the way. For there is more profit from their labor than from their death, and by their example they make others fear like punishments. But if when they are thus treated, they rebel and kick again, then forsooth they are slain as desperate wild beasts, whom neither prison nor chain could restrain and keep under. But they who take their bondage patiently are not left entirely hopeless. For if after they have been broken and tamed with long miseries, they show such repentance that it may be perceived that they are sorrier for their offense than for their punishment, sometimes by the prince's prerogative, and sometimes by the voice and consent of the people, their bondage either is mitigated,

[25] It is a little odd that More, advocate of suicide and divorce, both anathema to the ecclesiastical and civil opinion of his day, should be in full accord with his contemporaries on the question of a husband's full authority over his wife and his right to punish her if she displeased him. See also below, p. 165.

or else clean remitted and forgiven. He that makes a move toward adultery is in no less danger and jeopardy than if he had committed the adultery indeed. For in all offenses they count the intention and alleged purpose as evil as the act or deed itself, for they think that no interference ought to excuse him that did his best to succeed.

They set great store by fools. And as it is great reproach to do any of them hurt or injury, so they prohibit not the taking of pleasure in foolishness. For that, they think, does much good to the fools. And if any man is so serious and stern that he cannot laugh either at their words or at their deeds, none of them is committed to his care, for fear he would not order them gently and favorably enough, to whom they bring no pleasure (for other goodness in them is none)—much less yield him any profit.

To mock a man for his deformity, or because he lacks any part or limb of his body, is counted great dishonor and reproach, not to him that is mocked, but to him that mocks, who unwisely upbraids a man for a weakness which it was not in his power to escape. Also, as they count and reckon very little wisdom in him who cares not for natural beauty and comeliness, so to help the same with painting is taken for vain and wanton pride that brings great infamy. For they know, by very experience, that no comeliness or beauty does so highly commend and advance wives in the esteem of their husbands as honest character and lowliness. For as love is ofttimes won with beauty, so it is not kept, preserved, and continued, but by virtue and obedience.

They not only deter their people from doing evil by punishments, but also allure them to virtue with rewards of honor. For they set up in the market place the images of notable men, and of such as have been great and bountiful benefactors of the commonwealth, for the perpetual memory of their good acts, and also that the glory and renown of their ancestors may stir and provoke their posterity to virtue. He that inordinately and ambitiously strives for promotions is left all hopeless of ever attaining any promotion as long as he lives. They live together lovingly. For no magistrate is either haughty or fearful. Fathers they are called, and like fathers they behave. The citizens, as it is their duty, willingly pay to them due honor without any compulsion. Nor is the prince himself known from others by his apparel, or by a crown or diadem or cap of maintenance, but by a little sheaf of corn carried before him; as a taper of wax is borne before a bishop, whereby only he is known.

They have but few laws. For people so instructed and trained very few suffice. Yea, the thing they chiefly disapprove among other nations is that innumerable books of laws and expositions of the same are not sufficient. And they think it against all right and justice that men should be bound to laws, which are either in number more than can be read, or else blinder and darker than any man can well understand. Furthermore, they utterly exclude and banish all proctors and sergeants-at-law, who craftily handle cases, and subtly dispute of the laws. For they think it most fit that every man should plead his own cause, and tell the same tale before the judge that he would tell to his man of law. So shall there be less circumstance of words, and the truth shall sooner come to light when the judge with a discreet judgment weighs the words of him whom no lawyer has instructed in deceit, and when he helps and supports simple wits against the false and malicious circumventions of crafty persons. This is hard to observe in other countries, with so infinite a number of blind and intricate laws. But in Utopia every man is learned in the law. For, as I said, they have very few laws; and the plainer and more blunt that any interpretation is, that they approve as most just. For all laws, they say, are made and published only for the purpose that by them every man should be put in remembrance of his duty. But the crafty and subtle interpretation of them can put very few in that remembrance (for they are but few who understand them), whereas the simple, the plain and literal meaning of the laws is open to every man. Now as regards the vulgar sort of people, who are both most in number, and have most need to know their duties, were it not as good for them that no law were made at all, as that when it is made, so blind an interpretation should be put upon it, that without great wit and long arguing no man can discuss it? To the finding out of it, neither the plain judgment of the people can attain, nor can the whole lifetime of those who are occupied in working for their livings suffice thereto.

These virtues of the Utopians have caused their next neighbors and borderers, who live free and under no subjection (for the Utopians long ago delivered many of them from tyranny), to take magistrates from them, some for a year, and some for five years' space. These, when the time of their office is expired, they bring home again with honor and praise, and take new ones again with them into their country. These nations have undoubtedly very well and wholesomely provided for their commonwealths. For seeing that both the making and the marring of the public weal depend and hang upon the manners of the rulers and magistrates, what officers could they more wisely choose than those who cannot be led from honesty by bribes (for to men who shortly after shall depart thence into their own country, money would be unprofitable) nor yet be moved by favor or malice towards any man, as being strangers and unacquainted with the people? Which two vices of partiality and avarice, where they appear in judgments, immediately break down justice, the strongest and surest bond of a commonwealth. The peoples who fetch their officers and rulers from them, the Utopians call their fellows. And others to whom they have been beneficial, they call their friends.

As regards leagues, which in other places between country and country are so often concluded, broken, and made again, they make none with any nation. For what purpose serve these leagues? say they. As though nature had not set sufficient love between man and man. And who respects not nature, think you he will behave for words? They are led to this opinion chiefly, because in those parts of the world, leagues between princes are wont to be kept and observed very poorly. For here in Europe, and especially in these parts, where the faith and religion of Christ reign, the majesty of leagues is everywhere esteemed holy and inviolable, partly through the justice and goodness of princes, and partly through reverence for great bishops. Who, as they make no promise themselves, without very religiously performing the same, so they exhort all princes in every way to abide by their promises, and those who refuse or deny to do so,

by their pontifical power and authority they compel thereto. And surely they rightly think that it might seem a very reproachful thing, if in the leagues of those who by a special name are called faithful, faith should have no place.

But in that new-found part of the world, which is scarcely so far from us beyond the equator as our life and manners are dissident from theirs, no trust or confidence is placed in leagues. But the more and holier the ceremonies with which the league is knit up, the sooner it is broken by some quibbling found in the words, which many times are purposely so craftily inserted and placed that the bonds can never be so sure or so strong, but they will find some hole to open to creep out at, and break both league and truth. Which crafty dealing, yea which fraud and deceit, if they knew of it being practiced among private men in their bargains and contracts, they would straightway cry out at it with a sour countenance, as an offense most detestable, and worthy to be punished with a shameful death; yea, even they that profess themselves the authors of like counsel given to princes. Wherefore it may well be thought, either that all justice is but a base and low virtue, which keeps itself far down under the high dignity of kings; or at least, that there are two justices, one suited to the inferior sort of people, going afoot and creeping below on the ground, and bound down on every side with many bands so that it shall not run riot; the other a princely virtue, as it is of much higher majesty than the other poor justice, so also it has much more liberty, for which nothing is unlawful that it desires.

Princes of this kind, as I said, who are there such evil keepers of leagues, cause the Utopians, I suppose, to make no leagues at all. They perchance would change their minds if they lived here. Howbeit, they think that even when leagues are ever so faithfully observed and kept, yet the custom of making leagues was very evilly begun. For it causes men (as though nations which are separated by the space of a little hill or a river, were coupled together by no society or bond of nature) to think themselves born adversaries and enemies one to another, and that it is lawful for one to seek the death and destruction of the other, unless there is a league. Yea, and after the leagues are entered into, friendship does not grow and increase; but the liberty of robbing and stealing does still remain, as far as for lack of foresight and good counsel in writing the words of the league, any sentence or clause to the contrary is not therein sufficiently included. But the Utopians are of a contrary opinion. That is, that no man ought to be counted an enemy who has done no injury. And that the fellowship of nature is a strong league; and that men are better and more surely knit together by love and benevolence than by covenants of leagues; by hearty affection of mind rather than by words.[26]

[26] More here speaks of a "league" much as we should use the term "alliance." The actions of the European Powers, great and small, who were members of the League of Cambrai (1508), the Holy League (1511), and the Treaty of Universal Peace (1518), who made and broke promises and commitments at will, were sufficient to invoke the bitter irony that More shows in the foregoing passages. What his attitude would have been towards the associations of nations in our own day, it is difficult to say. He would almost certainly have been sympathetic with the ideal, but would doubtless still have cautioned against the "quibbling found in words" through which everyone can "find some hole open to creep out at."

Of warfare

They detest and abhor war or battle as a thing very beastly, although by no kind of beasts is it practiced so much as it is by man. And contrary to the custom of almost all other nations, they count nothing so inglorious as glory gotten in war. And therefore though they daily practice and exercise themselves in the discipline of war, and not only the men, but also the women upon certain appointed days, lest they should be wanting skill of arms, if need should require; yet they never go to battle except in defense of their own country, or to drive out of their friends' land the enemies that have invaded it, or by their power to deliver from the yoke and bondage of tyranny some people that is oppressed with tyranny. Which thing they do out of mere pity and compassion. Howbeit, they send help to their friends; not always in their defense, but sometimes also to requite and avenge injuries already done to them. But this they do not unless their counsel and advice in the matter are asked, while it is yet new and fresh. If they find the cause a just one, and if the other side will not restore again such things as are of them justly demanded, then they are the chief starters and makers of the war. Which they do, not only as often as booty is carried away by inroads and invasions of soldiers, but also with much more rancor, when their friends' merchants in any land, either under the cloak of unjust laws, or else by the wresting and misinterpretation of good laws, sustain an unjust accusation under color of justice.

Nor was the battle which the Utopians fought for the Nephelogetes against the Alaopolitanes, a little before our time, waged for any other cause but that the Nephelogete merchantmen, as the Utopians thought, suffered wrong from the Alaopolitanes, under pretense of right. But whether it were right or wrong, it was avenged with so cruel and mortal a war, the countries round about joining their help and power to the strength and malice of both parties that some of the most flourishing and wealthy nations were severely shaken, and some of them sharply beaten; nor were the mischiefs finished or ended until the Alaopolitanes at last yielded themselves up as bondmen unto the jurisdiction of the Nephelogetes. For the Utopians fought this war not for themselves. And yet the Nephelogetes before the war, when the Alaopolitanes flourished in wealth, were nothing to be compared with them.

So eagerly the Utopians prosecute the injuries done to their friends, yea, in money matters; but not their own likewise. For if by cunning or guile they are defrauded of their goods, so long as no violence is done to their bodies, they wreak their anger by abstaining from trading with that nation, until they have made satisfaction. Not because they set less store by their own citizens than by their friends, but because they feel the loss of their friends' money more heavily than the loss of their own. For their friends' merchants, since what they lose is their own private goods, suffer great damage by the loss. But their own citizens lose nothing but out of the common goods, and of something which was at home plentiful and almost superfluous, else it would not have been sent forth. Therefore no man feels the loss. And for this cause they think it too cruel an act to avenge that loss with the death of many men, when the inconvenience of the loss no man feels either in his life or his livelihood. But if it chance that any of their men in any other country is maimed or killed, whether it is done by public or private design, they discover and investigate the truth of the matter through their ambassadors, and unless the offenders are surrendered to them in recompense for the injury, they will not be appeased, but at once proclaim war against them. The offenders being yielded up, they punish them either with death or with bondage.

They are not only sorry but also ashamed to achieve a victory with much bloodshed, counting it great folly to buy precious wares too dear. They rejoice and boast if they vanquish and subdue their enemies by craft and deceit. For that feat they hold a general triumph, and, as if the matter were manfully handled, they set up a pillar of stone in the place where they thus vanquished their enemies, in token of their victory. For then they glory, then they boast and brag that they have played the man indeed, when they have overcome in a way that no other living creature but man could; that is to say, by the might and power of mind. For with bodily strength, say they, bears, lions, boars, wolves, dogs, and other wild beasts fight. And as most of them surpass us in strength and fierce courage, so in wit and reason we are much stronger than they all.

Their chief and principal purpose in war is to obtain the thing, which, if they had before obtained, they would not have waged battle. But if that is not possible, they take such cruel vengeance on those who are at fault that ever after they are afraid to do the like. This is their chief and principal purpose, which they immediately and first of all prosecute and carry forward, but in such manner that they show themselves to be more circumspect in avoiding and shunning dangers than desirous of praise and renown. Therefore, immediately after war is once solemnly declared, they contrive to have many proclamations, signed with their own common seal, set up secretly at one time in their enemies' land, in places most frequented. In these proclamations they promise great rewards to him who will kill their enemies' prince, and somewhat lesser gifts, but very great also, for every head of those whose names are contained in the said proclamations. They are those whom they count their chief adversaries, next to the prince. Whatever is promised to him who kills any of the proclaimed persons is doubled to him who brings any of the same to them alive. Yea, and to the proclaimed persons themselves, if they will change their minds and come over to them and join them, they offer the same great rewards, with pardon and assurance of their lives.

Therefore, it quickly comes to pass that their enemies hold all other men in suspicion, and are unfaithful and distrustful among themselves, one to another, living in great fear, and in no less jeopardy. For it is well known that many times most of them, and especially the prince himself, has been betrayed by those in whom they put their most hope and trust. So that there is no kind of act or deed that gifts and rewards do not impel men to. And to rewards they set no limit, but remembering and considering how great the hazard and peril to which they call them, they try to recompense the greatness of the danger with like great benefits. And therefore they promise not only wonderful great abundance of gold, but also lands of great revenues, lying in most safe places among their friends. And their promises they perform faithfully without any fraud or deceit.

This custom of buying and selling adversaries is disallowed among other people, as a cruel act of a base and cowardly mind. But the Utopians in this matter think themselves very praiseworthy, since like wise men they by this means despatch great wars without one battle or skirmish. Yea, they count it even a deed of pity and mercy, because by the death of a few offenders the lives of a great number of innocents, both of their own men, as also of their enemies, are ransomed and saved, who in fighting would have been slain. For they pity no less the common sort of their enemies' people than they do their own; knowing that they are driven to war against their wills by the furious madness of their princes and heads. But if by none of these means the affair proceeds as they would have it, then they contrive that causes of dispute and dissension are spread among their enemies, as by inciting the prince's brother, or some of the noblemen, to hope to obtain the kingdom. If in this way they prevail not, then they stir up the people that are next neighbors and borderers to their enemies, and them they set in their necks under color of some old title of right, such as kings are never without. To them they promise help and aid in their war. And as for money they give them abundance. But of their own citizens they send them few or none. For they make so much of them and love them so entirely that they would not be willing to change one of them for their adversary's prince. But their gold and silver, because they keep it all for this purpose only, they lay out frankly and freely, as who should live quite as wealthily, even if they bestowed it every penny.

Yea, and besides their riches, which they keep at home, they have also an infinite treasure abroad, since, as I said before, many nations are in their debt. Therefore they hire soldiers out of all countries, though chiefly of the Zapoletes, and send them to battle. This people lives five hundred miles from Utopia eastward. They are hideous, savage, and fierce, dwelling in wild woods and high mountains, where they were bred and brought up. They are of a hard nature, able to endure and sustain heat, cold, and labor, abhorring all delicate dainties, engaging in no agriculture or tillage of the ground, homely and rude both in the building of their houses and in their apparel, given to no goodness, but only to the breeding and bringing up of cattle. The most part of their living is gained by hunting and stealing. They are born only for war, which they diligently and earnestly seek for. And when they have gotten it, they are wondrous glad thereof. They go forth from their country in great companies together, and whoever lacks soldiers, to him they offer their service for small wages. This is the only craft that they have to get their living by. They maintain their life by seeking death. For them from whom they receive their wages they fight hardily, fiercely, and faithfully. But they bind themselves for no certain time. But on this condition they enter into contracts, that the next day they will take part with the other side for greater wages, and the day after that they will be ready to come back again for a little more money. There are few wars in those parts in which a great number of them are not engaged on both sides. Therefore it daily happens that near kinsfolk who were hired together on one side, and there carried on relations very friendly and familiarly with one another, shortly after, being separated into opposing sides, attack one another enviously and fiercely, and forgetting both kindred and friendship, thrust their swords in one another. And for no other cause but that they are hired by opposing princes for a little money, which they do so highly regard and esteem, that they will easily be persuaded to change sides for a halfpenny more wages by the day. So quickly have they acquired a taste for covetousness, which for all that is no profit to them. For what they get by fighting, immediately they spend unthriftily and wretchedly in riot.

This people fights for the Utopians against all nations, because they give them greater wages than any other nation will. For the Utopians, as they seek out good men to treat well, so they seek these evil and vicious men to abuse. When need requires it, with promises of great rewards they send them forth into great jeopardies, from which most of them never come back again to ask their rewards. But to them that remain alive they pay what they promised faithfully, that they may be more willing to put themselves in like dangers another time. Nor do the Utopians care how many of them they bring to destruction. For they believe that they would do a very good deed for all mankind, if they could rid the world of all that foul stinking den of most wicked and cursed people.

Next to these they use the soldiers of the people for whom they fight, and then the help of their other friends. And last of all they bring in their own citizens. To one among them of tried virtue and prowess they give the rule, governance, and conduct of the whole army. Under him they appoint two others, who, as long as he is safe, are both privates and out of office. But if he is taken or slain, one of the other two succeeds him, as it were by inheritance. And if the second is hurt, then the third takes his place, lest (as the chance of battle is uncertain and doubtful) the danger or death of the captain should bring the whole army into hazard. They choose soldiers, out of every city, those who offer themselves willingly. For they thrust no man into war against his will, because they believe if any man is fearful and faint-hearted by nature, he will not only do no manful and brave act himself, but will also be an occasion of cowardice to his fellows. But if any assault is made against their own country, then they put these cowards, who are strong-bodied, in ships among other bolder-hearted men. Or else they place them on the walls, whence they may not escape. Thus out of shame, since their enemies are at hand, and because they are without hope of running away, they forget all fear. And many times extreme necessity turns cowardice into prowess and manliness.

But as none of them is thrust out of his country into war against his will, so women that are willing to accompany their husbands in times of war are not prohibited or stopped.[27] Rather

---

[27] More again uses Plato as his guide. See *The Republic*, Book V (Classics Club edition, pp. 336-42).

they provoke and exhort them to it with praises. And in battle array the wives stand every one by her own husband's side. Also every man is surrounded with his own children, kinsfolk, and relatives by marriage; that they, whom nature chiefly moves to mutual succor, standing thus together, may help one another. It is a great reproach and dishonor for a husband to come home without his wife, or a wife without her husband, or a son without his father. And therefore, if the other side resists so hard that the battle comes to their hands, it is fought with great slaughter and bloodshed, even to the utter destruction of both parties. For as they employ all known means and shifts to keep themselves from the necessity of fighting, and to despatch the battle with hired soldiers, so when there is no remedy but they must needs fight themselves, then they fall to it courageously. For as long as they could, they wisely avoided it. Nor are they most fierce at the first onslaught, but as they fight, little by little their fierce courage increases with such stubborn and obstinate minds that they will rather die than yield an inch. For that security of life, which every man has at home, with no careful anxiety or concern how his posterity shall live after him (for this unhappy thought ofttimes breaks and weakens courageous stomachs), makes them stout and hardy, and disdainful to be conquered. Moreover, their knowledge of chivalry and feats of arms put them in good hope.

Finally, the wholesome and virtuous opinions wherein they were brought up even from their childhood, partly through learning and partly through the good ordinances and laws of their commonwealth, augment and increase their manly courage. By reason whereof they neither set so little store by their lives that they will rashly and unadvisedly cast them away, nor are they so far in ignorant and foolish love therewith that they will desire shamefully to keep them, when honor bids leave them. When the battle is hottest and in all places most fierce and fervent, a band of chosen and picked young men, who are sworn to live and die together, take upon themselves to destroy their adversary's captain. Him they attack, now with stealthy wiles, now by open strength. At him they strike both near and far off. He is assailed with a long and continuous assault, fresh men still coming in the wearied men's places. And seldom it happens, unless he save himself by flying, that he is not either slain, or else taken prisoner and surrendered to his enemies alive.

If the Utopians win the field, they do not pursue their enemies with a violent rage of slaughter. For they had rather take them alive than kill them. Neither do they so follow in chase and pursuit of their enemies that they leave not behind them one part of their host in battle array under their standards. Insomuch that if all their whole army be discomforted and overcome save the rear guard, and they therewith achieve the victory, then they had rather let all their enemies escape than follow them out of array. For, they remember how it has chanced unto themselves more than once, when the whole power and strength of their host was vanquished and put to flight, and their enemies, rejoicing in victory, were pursuing them fleeing some one way and some another, that a few of their men lying in an ambush, ready there for all occasions, have suddenly risen on the enemy,

thus dispersed and scattered out of array, and through presumption of safety unadvisedly pursuing the chase, and have straightway changed the fortune of the whole battle, and despite their
resistance have wrested out of their hands the sure and undoubted victory. They who a little before were conquered have
for their part conquered the conquerors.

It is hard to say whether they are craftier in laying an ambush
or cleverer in avoiding the same. You would think they intend
to retire, when that is the least of their intention. And contrariwise, when they go about that purpose, you would believe it
were least in their thoughts. For if they perceive themselves
either overmatched in number or closed in too narrow a place,
then they remove their camp, either in the night season with
silence, or by some trick deceive their enemies, or in the daytime
retire back so softly that it is no less jeopardy to meddle with
them when they retreat than when they press on. They fence
and fortify their camp securely with a deep and broad trench.
The earth therefrom is cast inward. Nor do they set drudges
and slaves at work about it. It is done by the hands of the soldiers
themselves. All the whole army works upon it, except those who
watch fully armed before the trench for surprise moves. Therefore by the labor of so many, a large trench closing in a great
compass of ground is made in less time than any man would
believe.

The armor or harness which they wear is sure and strong to
receive strokes, and fitted for all movements and gestures of the
body, insomuch that it is not unwieldy to swim in. For in the
discipline of their warfare, among other feats they learn to swim

in armor. Their weapons are arrows for long distance fighting, which they shoot both strongly and surely, not only the footmen, but also the horsemen. At hand strokes they use not swords but poleaxes, which are deadly, as well for sharpness as for weight, both in forward thrusts and down strokes. Engines for war they devise and invent wondrous cleverly, which when made they kept very secret, lest if they should be known before needed for use, they should be laughed at and serve no purpose. But in making them, they pay chief attention to this, that they be both easy to carry and handy to move and turn about.

Truce once made with their enemies for a short time, they do so firmly and faithfully keep that they will not break it; not even though they be thereunto provoked. They do not waste or destroy their enemies' land with foragings, or burn up their corn. Yea, they save it as much as may be from being overrun and trodden down either by men or horses, thinking that it grows for their own use and profit. They hurt no man who is unarmed, unless he be a spy. All cities that are surrendered to them they defend. And such as they win by force of assault, they neither despoil nor sack, but those who resisted and argued against the surrender of the same, they put to death; the other soldiers they punish with bondage. All the weak multitude they leave untouched. If they know that any citizens advised the yielding and surrender of the city, to them they give part of the condemned men's goods. The residue they distribute and give freely among them whose help they had in the same war. For not one of themselves takes any portion of the prey. But when the battle is finished and ended, they impose on their friends never a penny cost of all the charges they were at, but lay them upon the shoulders of the conquered. Them they burden with the whole charge of their expenses, which they demand of them partly in money, to be kept for like use in battle, and partly in lands bearing great revenues, to be paid unto them yearly forever. Such revenues they have now from many countries, which little by little, starting from divers and sundry causes, are increased above seven hundred thousand ducats [28] a year. To these countries they send forth some of their citizens as lieutenants, to live there sumptuously like men of honor and renown. And yet, this notwithstanding, much money is saved, which comes to the common treasury, unless it so chance that they had rather trust the country with the money. Which many times they do, until they have need to use it. And it seldom happens that they demand it all. Of these lands they assign a part to those who, at their request and exhortation, put themselves in such jeopardies as I spoke of before. If any prince stir up war against them, intending to invade their land, they meet him straightway outside their own borders with great power and strength. For they never lightly make war in their own countries. Nor are they ever brought into such extreme necessity as to take help from foreign lands into their own island.

[28] The gold ducat was first coined in Venice at the close of the thirteenth century. By More's time it was in general use in several European countries, being worth about 9s.4½d. There was an earlier Italian silver ducat worth considerably less.

Of the religions in Utopia

There are divers kinds of religion not only in sundry parts of the island, but also in divers places in every city. Some worship the sun as God; some, the moon; some, others of the planets. There are those who worship a man, who was once of excellent virtue and famous glory, not only as God, but also as the chiefest and highest God. But the most and wisest number, rejecting all these, believe that there is a certain divine power, unknown, everlasting, incomprehensible, inexplicable, far above the capacity and reach of man's wisdom, dispersed throughout the world, not in size, but in virtue and power. Him they call the Father of All. To him alone they attribute the beginnings, the increasings, the proceedings, the changes and the ends of all things. They give no divine honors to any other but to him. Yea, all the others also, though they are of divers opinions, yet on this point agree all together with the wisest, in believing that there is one chief and principal God, the maker and ruler of the whole world, whom they all commonly in their country call Mithra.[29] But on this point they disagree, so that among some he is counted one thing, and among some another. For every one of

[29] Just why More chose the Persian god Mithra as the deity whom the Utopians recognized is not clear, although it is consistent with his earlier statement that their language somewhat resembled the Persian; the widespread practice of the cult of Mithra in the early Christian era would make its presence on an unknown island plausible. Furthermore, its emphasis on the brotherhood of man, its recognition of faith, moral rectitude, and other virtues that are found also in Christian teachings mark it as a cult well qualified to suit More's purposes.

them, whatever it is which he takes for the chief God, thinks it to be the very same nature; to whose only divine might and majesty the sum and sovereignty of all things by the consent of all people is attributed and given.

Howbeit, they all begin now little by little to forsake and abandon this variety of superstitions, and to agree together in that religion which seems by reason to surpass and excel the rest. And it is not to be doubted that all the others would long ago have been abolished, except that whatever unfortunate thing happened to any of them, as he was considering a change in his religion, the fearfulness of the people took it not as a thing coming by chance, but as sent from God out of heaven; as though the God whose honor he was forsaking would avenge that wicked purpose against him. But after they heard us speak of the name of Christ, of his doctrine, laws, miracles, and of the no less wonderful constancy of so many martyrs, whose blood willingly shed brought a great number of nations throughout all parts of the world into their sect, you will not believe with what glad minds they agreed to the same, whether it were by the secret inspiration of God, or else because they thought it nearest that opinion which among them is counted chief. Howbeit, I think this was no small help and furtherance in the matter that they heard us say that Christ approved among his followers that all things be held in common; and that the same community of ownership does yet remain amongst the rightest Christian companies.[30]

[30] A note written in the margin of the original would seem to indicate that it is the monasteries that are meant here.

Verily, howsoever it came to pass, many of them consented to accept our religion, and were washed in the holy water of baptism. But because among us four (for no more of us were left alive, two of our company being dead) there was no priest, which I am right sorry for, they, though initiated and instructed in all other points of our religion, lack those sacraments which here none but priests administer. Howbeit, they understand and recognize them and are very desirous of the same. Yea, they reason and dispute the matter earnestly among themselves, whether without the sending of a Christian bishop, one chosen out of their own people may receive the order of priesthood. And truly they were minded to choose one. But at my departure from them they had chosen none. They also who do not agree to Christ's religion frighten no man from it, nor speak against any man who has received it, save one of our company who in my presence was sharply punished. He, as soon as he was baptized, began against our wills, with more zeal than wisdom, to reason on Christ's religion; and began to wax so hot on his subject that he not only praised our religion above all others, but also utterly despised and condemned all others, calling them profane, and the followers of them wicked and devilish and children of everlasting damnation. When he had thus long discoursed on the subject, they laid hold of him, accused him and condemned him to exile, not as a despiser of religion, but as a seditious person and an inciter of dissension among the people. For this is one of the most ancient laws among them, that no man shall be blamed for reasoning in the support of his own religion.

For King Utopus, even at the first beginning, hearing that the inhabitants of the land were, before his coming thither, in continual dissension and strife among themselves over their religions; perceiving also that this general dissension (since every separate sect took a different side in fighting for their country) was the only cause of his conquest of them all; as soon as he had gotten the victory, first of all made a decree that it should be lawful for every man to favor and follow whatever religion he would, and that he might do the best he could to lead others to his opinion, so long as he did it peaceably, gently, quietly, and soberly, without haste and contentious rebuking and denouncing others. If he could not by fair and gentle speech induce them to accept his opinion, still he should use no kind of violence and should refrain from unpleasant, seditious words. For him who would vehemently and fervently strive and contend for this cause was decreed banishment or bondage.

This law did King Utopus make, not only for the maintenance of peace, which he saw through continual contention and mortal hatred would be utterly extinguished, but also because he thought this decree would make for the furtherance of religion. On which he dared define and ordain nothing unadvisedly, as doubting whether God, desiring manifold and divers sorts of honor, might not inspire sundry men with sundry kinds of religion. And this he thought surely a very improper and foolish thing, and a sign of arrogant presumption, to compel all others by violence and threatenings to agree to the same that he believed to be true. Furthermore, though there is one religion which alone is true, and all others vain and superstitious, yet did he well foresee, that if the matter were handled with reason and sober modesty, the truth of its own power would at the last issue forth and come to light. But if contention and debate on that question should continue, as the worst men are most obstinate and stubborn, and in their evil opinion most constant, he perceived that the best and holiest religion would be trodden underfoot and destroyed by vain superstitions, even as good corn is by thorns and weeds overgrown and choked.

Therefore, all this matter he left undiscussed and gave to every man free liberty and choice to believe what he would. Saving that he earnestly and strictly charged them that no man should conceive so vile and base an opinion of the dignity of man's nature as to think that souls die and perish with the body, or that the world runs by chance, governed by no divine providence. And they believe that after this life vices are extremely punished and virtue bountifully rewarded. Him that is of a contrary opinion they count not in the number of mankind, but as one who has abased the high nature of his soul to the vileness of brute beasts' bodies; much less in the number of their citizens, whose laws and ordinances, if it were not for fear, he would not at all respect. For you may be sure he would study either with craft secretly to mock, or else violently to break the common laws of his country, in whom there remains no further fear but of the laws, nor any further hope beyond the body. Wherefore he that is thus minded is deprived of all honors, excluded from all offices and rejected from all public administration in the commonwealth. And he is despised by all sorts of people as of an unprofitable and base and vile nature. Howbeit, they give him no punishment, because they are persuaded that it is in no man's power to believe whatever he wishes. No, and they force him not by threatenings to dissemble his opinion and show a countenance contrary to his thought. For deceit and falsehood and all manner of lies, as next to fraud, they marvelously detest and abhor. But they suffer him not to discuss his opinions among the common people. But among the priests and men of gravity they do not only permit but also exhort him to dispute and argue, hoping that at last his madness will give place to reason.

There are also others, and of them no small number, who are not forbidden to speak their minds, since they ground their opinion upon some reason, and in their living are neither evil nor vicious. Their heresy is quite contrary to the other, for they believe that the souls of brute beasts are immortal and everlasting, but not to be compared to ours in dignity, nor ordained and predestined to a like felicity. For they all believe certainly and surely that man's bliss shall be so great that they mourn and lament everyone's sickness but no one's death, unless it is one whom they see depart his life reluctantly and against his will. For this they take as a very evil token, as though the soul were in despair and vexed in conscience, through some private and secret foreboding of punishment now at hand, and were afraid to depart. And they think he will not be welcome to God, if, when he is called, he runs not to him gladly, but is dragged by force and sore against his will.[31] They, therefore, who see this kind of death abhor it, and bury with sorrow and silence those

[31] More lived up to his precepts. See the account of his own death in Roper's *Life*, p. 277 ff.

who do so die. And when they have prayed God to be merciful
to the soul and mercifully to pardon the infirmities thereof, they
cover the dead corpse with earth. Contrariwise, for all who depart merrily and full of good hope, no man mourns, but follows
the hearse with joyful singing, commending the soul to God
with great affection. And at the last, not with a mourning sorrow but with a great reverence, they burn the body. And in the
same place they set up a pillar of stone, with the dead man's titles
thereon engraved. When they come home they relate his virtuous manners and his good deeds. But no part of his life is so oft
or so gladly talked of as his merry death.

They think that this remembrance of his virtue and goodness
vehemently encourages and strengthens the living to virtue,
and that nothing can be more pleasant and acceptable to the
dead, whom they suppose to be present among them when they
talk of them, though to the dull and feeble eyesight of mortal
men they are invisible. For it were a hardship if the blessed were
not at liberty to go whither they would. And it were a mark of
great unkindness in them to utterly cast away the desire of
visiting and seeing their friends, to whom they were in their
lifetime joined by mutual love and charity. For this in good
men after their death they count is increased rather than diminished. They believe therefore that the dead are personally present
among the living, as beholders and witnesses of all their words
and deeds. Therefore, they go more courageously to their business, having a trust and confidence in such overseers. And this
same belief in the presence of their forefathers and ancestors
among them makes them shrink from all secret dishonesty.

They utterly despise and mock at soothsayings and divinations of things to come by the flight or the voices of birds, and all other divinations of vain superstition, which in other countries are given much attention. But they highly esteem and worship miracles that come outside the regular course of nature, as works and witnesses of the present power of God. And these they say happen very often. And sometimes in great and doubtful matters, by common intercession and prayers, they procure and obtain them with a sure hope and confidence and steadfast belief.

They think that the contemplation of nature and the praise which grows out of it are to God a very acceptable honor. Yet there are many so earnestly bent and devoted to religion that they care nothing for learning, nor give their minds to any knowledge of secular things. But idleness they utterly shun and avoid, thinking felicity after this life is won and obtained by busy labors and good exercises. Some of them, therefore, tend the sick, some mend highways, clean ditches, repair bridges, dig turfs, gravel and stones, fell and cleave wood, bring wood, corn, and other things into the cities in carts, and serve not only in public works but also in private labors as servants, yea, more than bondmen. For whatsoever unpleasant, hard, and vile work is anywhere being done, the labor, loathsomeness, and desperation of which frighten others, all that they take on themselves willingly and gladly, securing the quiet and rest of others, but remaining in continual work and labor themselves, and not upbraiding others therefor. They neither reprove other men's lives, nor glory in their own. The more like servants these men behave themselves, the more they are honored of all men.

They are divided into two sects, the one that lives single and chaste, abstaining not only from the company of women, but also from the eating of flesh, and some of them from all manner of beasts. They utterly reject the pleasures of this present life as hurtful, and are wholly set upon desire of the life to come, hoping by watching and sweating shortly to obtain it, and being in the meantime merry and lusty. The other sect is no less desirous of labor, but they embrace matrimony, not despising the solace thereof, and thinking they cannot be relieved of their bounden duties towards nature without labor and toil, nor towards their native country without procreation of children. They abstain from no pleasure that does not hinder them from labor. They love the flesh of four-footed beasts, because they believe that by that meat they are made hardier and stronger to work. The Utopians count this sect the wiser, but the other the holier. If their preference for a single life before matrimony, and a sharp life before an easier life, were grounded upon reason, they would mock them. But now, inasmuch as they say they are led to it by religion, they honor and worship them. And they call them by a peculiar name, Buthrescas, which word by interpretation signifies to us men of religion or religious men.

They have priests of exceeding holiness, and therefore very few. For there are but thirteen in every city according to the number of their churches, save when they go forth to battle. For then seven of them go forth with the army; in whose stead as many new are created at home. But the others at their return home again re-enter every one his own place, those that are above the number, until such time as they succeed to the places of the others at their dying, are in the meantime continually in the company of the bishop. For he is the chief head of them all. They are chosen by the people, as the other magistrates are, by secret voting, for the avoiding of strife. After their election they are consecrated by their own company. They are overseers of all divine matters, orderers of religious ceremonies, and, as it were, judges and masters of manners. And it is a great dishonor and shame to be rebuked or spoken to by any of them for dissolute and incontinent living. But whereas it is their office to give good exhortations and counsel, it is the duty of the prince and the other magistrates to correct and punish offenders, except that the priests excommunicate from having any part in divine matters those whom they find exceedingly vicious livers. And there is almost no punishment more feared among them. For they fall into very great infamy, and are inwardly tormented with a secret fear of religion, and do not long escape free with their bodies. For unless by quick repentance they prove the amendment of their lives to the priests, they are taken and punished by the council, as wicked and irreligious.

Both childhood and youth are instructed and taught by them. Nor are they more diligent to instruct them in learning than in virtue and good manners. For they use very great endeavor and diligence to put into the heads of their children while they are yet tender and pliant, good opinions, profitable for the conservation of their public weal, which when they are once rooted in children, remain with them all their life after, and are wondrous profitable for the defense and maintenance of the state of the commonwealth, which never decays but through vices arising from evil opinions. The priests, unless they are women (for they are not excluded from priesthood, howbeit few are chosen, and none but widows and old women), the men priests, I say, take for their wives the chiefest women in all their country. For to no office among the Utopians is more honor and pre-eminence given. Insomuch that if priests commit any offense, they come under no public judgment, but are left only to God and themselves. For they think it not lawful to touch with a man's hand one who though never so vicious was so specially dedicated and consecrated to God, as a holy offering.

This custom they may easily observe, because they have so few priests, and choose them with such circumspection. For it scarcely ever chances that the most virtuous among a virtuous people, who by reason only of his virtue was advanced to so high a dignity, can fall to vice and wickedness. And if it should chance indeed—as man's nature is mutable and frail—yet because they are so few and promoted to no might or power but only honor, it is not to be feared that any great damage should happen and ensue from them to the commonwealth. They have such rare and few priests, lest if the honor were communicated to many, the dignity of the order, which among them now is so highly esteemed, should fall into contempt. Especially because they think it hard to find many persons so good as to be fit for that dignity, to the execution and discharge whereof it is not sufficient to be endowed with mediocre virtues.

Furthermore, these priests are not more esteemed by their own countrymen than they are by foreign and strange countries.

Which thing may hereby plainly appear. And I think also that this is the cause of it. While the armies are fighting together in open field, the priests a little to one side kneel upon their knees in their hallowed vestments, holding up their hands to heaven and praying first of all for peace, next for victory for their own side, but for neither side a bloody victory. If their host get the upper hand, they run into the thick of the fight and restrain their own men from slaying and cruelly pursuing their vanquished enemies. If these enemies do but see and speak to them, it is enough for the safeguard of their lives. And the touching of their clothes defends and saves all their goods from plunder and spoil. This thing has raised them to such great worship and true majesty among all nations that many times they have safely preserved their own citizens from the cruel force of their enemies, or else their enemies from the furious rage of their own men. For it is well known that when their own army has recoiled and in despair turned back and run away, while their enemies fiercely pursued with slaughter and spoil, then the priests coming between have stayed the murder, and parted both the hosts. So that peace has been made and concluded between both sides upon equal and impartial terms. For there was never any nation so fierce, so cruel and rude, but held them in such reverence that they counted their bodies hallowed and sanctified, and therefore not to be violently and unreverently touched.

The Utopians keep holy the first and the last day of every month and year, dividing the year into months, which they measure by the course of the moon, as they do the year by the course of the sun. The first days they call in their language

Cynemernes and the last Trapeme‿nes, which words may be interpreted, primifest and finifest, or else in our speech, first feast and last feast. Their churches are very gorgeous and not only of fine and elaborate workmanship, but also—which in view of the fewness of them was necessary—very wide and large, and able to receive a great company of people. But they are all somewhat dark. Howbeit, that was not the effect of ignorance in building, but as they say, by the counsel of the priests, because they thought that overmuch light disperses men's cogitations, whereas in dim and doubtful light they are collected and more earnestly fixed upon religion and devotion. Although religion is not there the same among all men, yet all the kinds and fashions of it, though they are sundry and manifold, agree together in honor of the divine nature, going divers ways to one end. Therefore nothing is seen or heard in the churches, which seems not to agree impartially with them all. If there is a distinct kind of sacrament peculiar to any one sect, that they perform at home in their own houses. The public sacraments are so ordered that they are no derogation or prejudice to any of the private rites and religions. Therefore, no image of any god is seen in the church, to the intent it may be free for every man to conceive God by his religion after what likeness and similitude he will.

They call upon no peculiar name of God, but only Mithra,[32] in which word they all agree on one nature of the divine majesty, whatsoever it may be. No prayers are used but such as

[32] See above, p. 152, footnote 29

every man may boldly pronounce without offending any sect.
They come to the church the last day of every month and year,
in the evening still fasting, there to give thanks to God for
having prosperously passed over the year or month, of which
that holy day is the last day. The next day they come to the
church early in the morning, to pray to God that they may
have good fortune and success all the new year or month which
they begin on that same holy day. But on the holy days that are
the last days of the months and years, before they come to the
church, the wives fall down prostrate before their husbands'
feet at home and the children before the feet of their parents,
confessing and acknowledging that they have offended either
by some actual deed, or by the omission of their duty, and desire pardon for their offense. Thus, if any cloud of secret ill-
feeling was risen at home, by this satisfaction it is blown away,
that they may be present at the rites with pure and charitable
minds. For they are afraid to come there with troubled consciences. Therefore, if they know themselves to bear any hatred
or grudge toward any man, they presume not to come to the
sacrament, before they have reconciled themselves and purged
their consciences, for fear of great vengeance and punishment
for their offense.

When they come thither, the men go to the right side of the
church and the women to the left side. There they place themselves in such order that all those of the male kind in every
household sit before the goodman of the house, and those of
the female kind before the goodwife. Thus it is provided that
all their gestures and behavior are marked and observed abroad

by those by whose authority and discipline they are governed at home. This also they diligently see to, that the younger evermore is coupled with his elder, lest if children are joined together, they pass the time in childish wantonness, wherein they ought principally to conceive a religious and devout fear towards God, which is the chief and almost the only incitement to virtue.

They kill no living beast in sacrifice, nor do they think that the merciful clemency of God delights in blood and slaughter, which has given life to beasts to the intent they should live. They burn frankincense and other sweet savors, and light also a great number of wax candles and tapers, not supposing these things to be anything necessary to the divine nature, any more than the prayers of men are. But this unhurtful and harmless kind of worship pleases them. And by these sweet savors and lights and other such ceremonies men feel themselves secretly lifted up and encouraged to devotion with more willing and fervent hearts.

The people in church wear white apparel. The priest is clothed in changeable colors, which in workmanship are excellent but in stuff not very precious. For their vestments are neither embroidered with gold nor set with precious stones, but are wrought so finely and cunningly with divers feathers of birds, no costly stuff can equal the price of the work. Furthermore, in these birds' feathers and in the due order of them, which is observed in their setting, is contained, they say, certain divine mysteries. The interpretation whereof is diligently taught by the priests that they may be put in remembrance of the bountiful benefits of God to them, and of the love and honor which on their behalf is due to God; and also of their duties one to another.

When the priest first comes out of the vestry thus appareled, they fall down straightway every one reverently to the ground, with such still silence on every one's part that the very manner of the thing strikes into them a certain fear of God, as though he were personally present. When they have lain a little space on the ground, the priest gives them a sign to rise. Then they sing praises unto God, which they intermix with instruments of music, for the most part unlike those which we use in this part of the world. And as some of ours are much sweeter than theirs, so some of theirs far surpass ours. But in one thing doubtless they go exceedingly far beyond us. For all their music, both what they play upon instruments, and what they sing with man's voice, does so resemble and express natural emotions, the sound and tune are so applied and made harmonious to the words, that whether it be a prayer, or a ditty of gladness, of patience, of trouble, of mourning, or of anger, the fashion of the melody does so represent the meaning of the thing that it does wonderfully move, stir, pierce, and inflame the hearers' minds.[33] At the end the people and the priest together repeat solemn

[33] There is a suggestion of the same idea in Plato (*The Republic,* Book III, Classics Club edition, pp. 288-9). But this bears an even closer resemblance to Cicero, who said: "Rhythm and melody give imitations of anger and gentleness, and also of courage and temperance, and of virtues and vices in general which hardly fall short of the actual affections . . . for in listening to such strains our souls undergo a change. . . . The musical modes differ essentially from one another, and those who hear them are differently affected by each."—*Politics,* Jowett trans., 1905, VIII, 5.

prayers in words, pronounced in set phrases, so made that every man may privately apply to himself that which is publicly spoken by all.

In these prayers every man recognizes and acknowledges God to be his maker, his governor, and the principal cause of all other goodness, thanking him for so many benefits received at his hand, but chiefly that through the favor of God he has chanced to be in that commonwealth which is most happy and well ordered, and has chosen that religion which he hopes to be most true. In which respect if he errs, or if there is any other better than either of them and more acceptable to God, he desires him that he will of his goodness let him have knowledge thereof, as one who is ready to follow what way soever he will lead him. But if this form and fashion of commonwealth is best, and his own religion most true and perfect, then he desires God to give him a constant steadfastness in the same, and to bring all other people to the same order of living and to the same opinion of God, unless there is something in this diversity of religions that delights his inscrutable pleasure. In brief, he prays him that after death he may come to him, but how soon or late he dares not assign or determine. Howbeit, if it might agree with his majesty's pleasure, he would be much gladder to die a painful death and so go to God, than by long living in worldly prosperity to stay away from him. When this prayer is said, they fall down to the ground again and a little after rise up and go to dinner. And the rest of the day they pass in play and military exercise.

Now I have declared and described unto you, as truly as I

could, the form and order of that commonwealth, which verily in my judgment is not only the best, but also that which alone of good right may claim and take upon itself the name of commonwealth or public weal. For in other places they speak still of the commonwealth, but every man procures his own private wealth. Here, where nothing is private, the common interests are earnestly looked to. And truly on both accounts they have good cause to do as they do. For in other countries, who knows that he will not starve for hunger, unless he make some private provision for himself, even though the commonwealth flourish never so much in riches? And, therefore, he is compelled even of very necessity to pay regard to himself rather than to the people, that is to say, to others. Contrariwise, where all things are common to every man, it is not doubted that no man shall lack anything necessary for his private use, so long as the common storehouses and barns are sufficiently stored. For there nothing is distributed in a niggardly fashion, nor is there any poor man or beggar. And though no man owns anything, yet every man is rich. For what can be more rich than to live joyfully and merrily, without grief and worry, not concerned for his own living, nor vexed and troubled with his wife's importunate complaints, nor dreading poverty for his son, nor sorrowing for his daughter's dowry? Yea, they take no care at all for the living and wealth of themselves and all theirs, their wives, their children, their nephews, their children's children, and all the succession that ever shall follow in their posterity.

And, besides this, there is no less provision for those who were at once laborers and are now weak and impotent than for those who now labor and bear the burden. Here now I would see, if any man dare be so bold as to compare with this equity the justice of other nations; among whom, may I perish utterly, if I can find any sign or token of equity and justice! For what justice is this, that a rich goldsmith,[34] or usurer, or to be brief, any one of those who either do nothing at all, or else something that is not very necessary to the commonwealth, should have a pleasant and wealthy living, either in idleness, or in unnecessary business, when meanwhile poor laborers, carters, ironsmiths, carpenters, and plowmen, by such great and continual toil, as beasts of burden are scarce able to sustain, and again such necessary toil that without it no commonwealth would be able to continue and endure one year, yet get so hard and poor a living and live so wretched and miserable a life that the state and condition of the laboring beasts may seem much better and more comfortable? For they are not put to such continual labor, nor is their living much worse; yea, for them it is much pleasanter, for they take no thought in the meantime for the future. But these ignorant, poor wretches are now tormented with barren and unfruitful labor, and the remembrance of their poor, indigent, and beggarly old age kills them off. For their daily wage is so little that it will not suffice for the same day, much less yield any overplus that may daily be laid up for the relief of old age.

Is not this an unjust and an unkind commonwealth, which

[34] The goldsmiths until the end of the seventeenth century played a part in the economic life of the country far beyond the confines of their own craft. They were also bankers, receiving deposits, supplying loans, and dealing in foreign coins and bullion, and in bills of exchange.

gives great fees and rewards to gentlemen, as they call them, and to goldsmiths, and to others who are either idle persons, or else only flatterers, and devisers of vain pleasures; and on the other hand, makes no considerate provision for poor plowmen, colliers, laborers, carters, ironsmiths, and carpenters, without whom no commonwealth can continue? But when it has misused the labors of their lusty and flowering age, at the last when they are oppressed with old age, sickness, needy, poor, and indigent of all things, then forgetting their many painful watchings, nor remembering their many and great benefits, it recompenses and requites them most unkindly with a miserable death.[35]

And yet, in addition to this, the rich not only by private fraud, but also by public laws, every day pluck and snatch away from the poor some part of their daily living. So whereas it seemed previously unjust to recompense with unkindness the toils that have been beneficial to the public weal, the rich have now to this their wrong and unjust dealing—which is a much worse act —given the name of justice, yea, and that by force of law. Therefore, when I consider and weigh in my mind all these commonwealths, which nowadays flourish everywhere, so God help me, I can perceive nothing but a certain conspiracy of rich men procuring their own comforts under the name and title of the commonwealth. They invent and devise all means and

---

[35] Between the period of the Black Death (1348-49) and the first Statute of Laborers (1351), there had been no fewer than fourteen acts of parliament dealing with workingmen. But like the first one, they were all in the interests of the employer, and those which treated of wages set down maximum not minimum wages to be paid. Legislation under Elizabeth was to furnish some protection but that did not come for many years after More wrote.

schemes, first how to keep safely, without fear of losing what they have unjustly gathered together, and next, how to hire and misuse the work and labor of the poor for as little money as may be. When the rich men decreed these devices to be kept and observed for the commonwealth's sake, that is to say, for the wealth also of the poor, then they are made laws.

Yet these most wicked and vicious men, when they have by their insatiable covetousness divided among themselves all the things which would have sufficed everyone, still how far are they from the wealth and felicity of the Utopian commonwealth! From which, in that all desire of money and use thereof are utterly excluded and banished, how great a heap of cares is cut away! How great a cause of wickedness and mischief is plucked up by the roots! For who does not know that fraud, theft, rapine, brawling, quarreling, brabling, strife, chiding, contention, murder, treason, poisoning, which by daily punishments are rather avenged than restrained, die when money dies? And also that fear, grief, care, labors and watchings perish even the very moment that money perishes? Yes, poverty itself, which only seemed to lack money, if money were gone, would also decrease and vanish away.

And that you may perceive this more plainly, consider yourselves some barren and unfruitful year, wherein many thousands of people have starved for hunger. I dare be bold to say that at the end of that penury so much corn and grain would have been found in the rich men's barns, if they had been searched, that if it had been divided among those whom famine and pestilence killed, no man at all would have felt that plague and penury. So easily might men get their living, if that same worthy princess, Lady Money, did not alone stop up the way between us and our livelihood, though she in God's name was excellently devised and invented, in order that by her the way thereto should be opened. I am sure the rich perceive this, nor are they ignorant how much better it would be to lack no necessary thing than to abound with overmuch superfluity; to be rid of innumerable cares and troubles than to be beseiged with great riches.

And I doubt not that either respect for every man's private comfort, or else the authority of our saviour Christ (which for his great wisdom could not but know what was best, and for his inestimable goodness could not but counsel that which he knew to be best) would have brought all the world long ago unto the laws of this commonwealth, if it were not that one single beast, the princess and mother of all mischief, Pride, resists and hinders it. She measures not wealth and prosperity by her own well being, but by the miseries and discomforts of others; she would not of her own will be made a goddess, if there were no wretches left whom she might be lady over to mock and scorn, over whose miseries her felicity might shine, and whose poverty she might vex, torment, and increase by gorgeously vaunting her riches. This hell-hound creeps into men's hearts, and plucks them back from entering the right path of life, and is so deeply rooted in men's breasts that she cannot be plucked out.

This form and fashion of a commonwealth, which I would gladly wish for all nations, I am glad at least that it has chanced to the Utopians, who have followed those institutions of life whereby they have laid such foundations for their state as shall continue and last not only happily, but also, as far as man's wit may judge and conjecture, endure forever. For seeing that the chief causes of ambition and sedition with other vices are plucked up by the roots and abandoned at home, there can be no danger of civil strife, which alone has cast underfoot and brought to nought the well-fortified and strongly defended wealth and riches of many cities. And forasmuch as perfect concord remains, and wholesome laws are executed at home, the envy of all foreign princes is not able to shake or move the empire, though they have many times long ago gone about to do it, being evermore driven back.

When Raphael had thus made an end of his tale, many things came to my mind, which in the manners and laws of that people seemed to be instituted and founded on no good reason, not only the fashion of their military arts, their rites and religions, and others of their laws, but also, yea and chiefly, that which is the principal foundation of all their ordinances, that is to say, the community of their life and living, without any use of money, by which practice alone all the nobility, magnificence, worship, honor and majesty, the true ornaments and honors, as the common opinion is, of a commonwealth, are utterly overthrown and destroyed. Yet because I knew that he was weary of talking, and was not sure whether he could bear that anything should be said against his opinion; and especially because I remembered that he had blamed this fault in others, who are afraid lest they seem not wise enough, unless they can find some fault in other men's inventions; therefore, I praising both their institutions and his account of them took him by the hand and led him in to supper, saying that we would choose another time to weigh and examine the same matters, and talk with him more at length thereon: which would to God it may some day come to pass. In the meantime, as I cannot agree and consent to all the things that he said, though he is without doubt a man singularly well learned, and in all worldly matters exactly and profoundly experienced, so must I needs confess and grant that there are many things in the Utopian commonwealth which in our cities I may rather wish than hope for.

Thus ended the afternoon's talk of Raphael Hythloday concerning the laws and institutions of the Island of Utopia.

To the Right Honorable Jerome Busleiden,[1] *Provost*
of Arienn, and Councilor to the Catholic King
Charles, Peter Giles, Citizen of Antwerp, wishes
health and felicity.

T HOMAS MORE, the unique ornament of this our age, as
you yourself, right honorable Busleiden, to whom he is
perfectly well known, can witness, sent me the other day the
Island of Utopia, well known to very few as yet, but most
worthy; which, as it far excels Plato's commonwealth, all
people should wish to know; especially since it is so finely
described, and so cunningly painted by a man most eloquent;
and so clear to the eye that as oft as I read it, methinks I see
somewhat more than when I heard Raphael Hythloday himself (for I was present at that talk as well as Master More)
uttering and pronouncing his own words. Yea, even though the
man, with his simple eloquence, did so explain and declare the
matter that he plainly enough appeared to be reporting not
things which he had learned of others only by hearsay, but what
he had with his own eyes seen and thoroughly viewed, and
with which he had a long time been acquainted. A man he is

1 Jerome Busleiden was a wealthy cleric of Brussels, founder of the College of
the Three Languages (Hebrew, Greek, and Latin) at Louvain, who became
a great friend of More while he was on the mission to Flanders with Tunstall.

truly, in my opinion, as regards the knowledge of regions, peoples, and worldly experience, much surpassing even the very famous and renowned traveler Ulysses; such a one indeed as for the space of these eight hundred years past I think nature has not brought forth his like into the world; in comparison with whom Vespucci [2] may be thought to have seen nothing. Moreover, whereas we are wont to declare and express more effectually and pithily things that we have seen than those which we have only heard, there was besides that in this man a certain peculiar grace and singular dexterity in describing and setting forth the matter withal.

Yet the selfsame things as oft as I behold and consider them drawn and painted with Master More's pencil, I am therewith so moved, so delighted, so inflamed, and so rapt, that sometimes methinks I am actually present in the Island of Utopia. And, I promise you, I can scarce believe that Raphael himself in all that five years' space that he was abiding in Utopia, saw there so much as here in Master More's description is to be seen and perceived. Which description is filled with so many wonders and miraculous things that I stand in great doubt at what first and chiefly to muse or marvel: whether at the excellence of his perfect and sure memory, which could well-nigh word by word repeat so many things heard only once; or else at his singular sagacity, who so well and wisely remarked and accounted for all the original causes and reasons—to vulgar people commonly unknown—wherefrom issue and spring the

[2] See p. 18, footnote 3.

mortal confusion and utter decay of a commonwealth, and wherefrom also the advancement and wealthy state of the same may rise and grow; or else at the efficacy and pith of his words, which in so fine a Latin style, with such force of eloquence, have couched together and comprehended so many diverse matters, especially being a man continually encumbered with so many busy and troublesome cares, both public and private, as he is. Howbeit, all these things will cause you little to marvel, right honorable Busleiden, for you are familiarly and thoroughly acquainted with the notable, yea almost divine, wit of the man.

But now to proceed to other matters. I surely know nothing needful or requisite to be added to his writings, but a meter of four verses written in the Utopian tongue, which, after Master More's departure, Hythloday by chance showed me, and which I have caused to be added thereto,[3] with the alphabet[4] of the same nation. For, as regards the situation of the island, that is to say, in what part of the world Utopia lies, the ignorance and lack whereof not a little troubles and grieves Master More; indeed Raphael left that not unspoken of. Howbeit, with very few words he lightly touched on it, passing it over incidentally and by the way, as if to keep and reserve it to another place. And his words, I know not how, by a certain evil and unlucky chance, escaped us both. For when Raphael was speaking thereof, one of Master More's servants came to him and whispered in his ear. Wherefore, I was then all the more

3 See p. 181.
4 See "The Printer to the Reader," p. 182.

anxious to hear, but one of the company, by reason of a cold taken, I think, on shipboard, coughed out so loud that he took from my hearing certain of his words. But I will never pause or rest until I have got the full and exact knowledge thereof; so far that I will be able perfectly to instruct you, not only in the longitude or true meridian of the island, but also in the right latitude thereof, that is to say, in the elevation or height of the pole in that region—if our friend Hythloday is in safety and alive. For we hear very uncertain news of him. Some report that he died on his journey homeward. Some again affirm that he returned to his own country, but partly because he could not endure the fashions of his countrymen and partly because his mind and affection was altogether set and fixed upon Utopia, they say he has taken his voyage thitherward again. Now as regards the point that the name of this island is nowhere found among the old and ancient cosmographers, this doubt Hythloday himself very well dispelled. "For it is possible enough," quoth he, "that the name, which it had in old time was afterward changed, or else that they never had knowledge of this island; since now in our time divers lands are found, which to the old geographers were unknown."

Howbeit, what need is there on its behalf to fortify the matter with arguments, seeing Master More is author hereof sufficient? And whereas he doubted whether to edit or print the book, indeed herein I both commend and acknowledge the man's modesty. Howbeit, to me it seems a work most unworthy to be long suppressed, and most worthy to go abroad into the hands of men, yea, and under title of your name to be published to the world; both because the singular endowments and qualities of Master More are to no man better known than to you, and also because no man is more fit and meet than you with good counsels to further and advance the common-wealth, wherein you have many years already contin-ually labored with great glory and commendation, both for wisdom and knowledge and also for integrity and uprightness. Thus, O liberal supporter of good learning and flower of this our time, I bid you most heartily farewell. At Antwerp, 1516, the first day of November.

*A Meter Of IIII Verses In The Utopian Tongue,
briefly touching both the strange beginning and also
the happy and wealthy continuance of the same
commonwealth.*

Utopos 'na Boccas peu la chama polta chamaan.
Bargol he maglomi baccan soma gymnosophaon.
Agrama gymnosophon labarem bacha bodamilomin.
Voluala barchin heman la lauoluala dramme pagloni.

*Which verses the translator according to his simple knowledge
and poor understanding of the Utopian tongue has thus roughly
Englished:*

My king and conqueror, Utopus by name,
A prince of much renown and immortal fame,
Has made of me an isle that erst no island was,
Frought full of worldly wealth, pleasure and solace.
I, the one of all without philosophy,
Have shaped for man a philosophical city.
As I in me have nothing dangerous to impart,
So better to receive I am ready with all my heart.

THE PRINTER TO THE READER

*The Utopian alphabet, good Reader, which is prom-
ised in the above written epistle,[5] I have not now
added here, because I have not as yet the true characters or forms of the Utopian letters. And no marvel,
seeing it is a tongue much stranger to us than the
Indian, the Persian, the Syrian, the Arabic, the
Egyptian, the Macedonian, the Slavonian,
the Cyprian, the Scythian, etc. Which
tongues, though they are nothing
so strange among us as the Utopian
is, yet their characters we have
not. But, I trust, God willing,
at the next printing hereof,
to perform that which now
I can not; that is to say,
to exhibit perfectly to
thee the Utopian
alphabet. In the
meantime ac-
cept my good
will. And
so fare
well.*

δ The letter from Peter Giles to Jerome Busleiden, p. 176.

LETTER OF ERASMUS TO
ULRICH VON HUTTEN

LETTER OF ERASMUS TO
ULRICH VON HUTTEN

The interest aroused by the *Utopia* on the continent led at once to curiosity and speculation about its author, the Englishman, Thomas More, as yet known on the European side of the Channel only to a few diplomats and a small group of ecclesiastical and literary friends. Erasmus, on the contrary, who had seen the first edition of the *Utopia* through the press for his friend, was already a figure well known to everyone in the literary world. It was quite natural, therefore, that his acquaintances in Holland, France, and the Germanies, should deluge him with questions regarding the author whose work he had sponsored. It was in answer to such a request from the fiery German knight, Ulrich von Hutten, later a sworn foe of Erasmus but then his friend, that the following letter was written. It is not only the earliest biographical account of More extant, but to some, the most satisfying.

Certainly no one was better qualified to write of More than the great Dutch scholar. The friendship between the two men had begun with their first meeting in 1499 and was to last until More's death in 1535. For weeks at a time on his visits to England, Erasmus was a member of More's household, and of their congeniality of mind and spirit, the writings of both can leave no doubt. When the news of More's execution reached Erasmus, he said, "In More's death I seem to have died myself; we had but one soul between us."

This biographical letter appeared first in 1519, in a collection of letters of Erasmus that were published in that year; and it is usually assigned to that date. Some grounds exist for attributing it to a somewhat earlier date, 1517, but the evidence is not conclusive.

Desiderius Erasmus to Ulrich von Hutten

𝕸OST ILLUSTRIOUS Hutten, your love—I had almost said your passion—for the genius of Thomas More,
kindled as it is by his writings, which, as you truly say, are as
learned and witty as anything can possibly be, is, I assure you,
shared by many others; and moreover the feeling in this case is
mutual; since More is so delighted with what you have written,
that I myself am almost jealous of you. It is an example of what
Plato says of that sweetest wisdom, which excites much more
ardent love among men than the most admirable beauty of
form. It is not discerned by the eye of sense, but the mind has
eyes of its own, so that even here the Greek saying holds true,
that out of Looking grows Liking; and so it comes to pass that
people are sometimes united in the warmest affection, who have
never seen or spoken to each other. And as it is a common experience that for some unexplained reason different people are attracted by different kinds of beauty, so between one mind and
another, there may seem to be a sort of latent kindred, which
causes us to be specially delighted with some and not with
others.

As to your asking me to paint you a full-length portrait of
More, I only wish my power of satisfying your request were
equal to your earnestness in pressing it. For to me too it will be
no unpleasant task to linger awhile in the contemplation of a

friend, who is the most delightful character in the world. But, in the first place, it is not given to every man to be aware of all More's accomplishments; and in the next place, I know not whether he will himself like to have his portrait painted by any artist that chooses to do so. For indeed I do not think it easier to make a likeness of More than of Alexander the Great, or of Achilles; neither were those heroes more worthy of immortality. The hand of an Apelles [1] is required for such a subject, and I am afraid I am more like a Fulvius or a Rutuba [2] than an Apelles. Nevertheless I will try to draw you a sketch, rather than a portrait, of the entire man, so far as daily and domestic intercourse has enabled me to observe his likeness and retain it in my memory. But if some diplomatic employment should ever bring you together, you will find out how poor an artist you have chosen for this commission; and I am afraid you will think me guilty of envy or of wilful blindness in taking note of so few out of the many good points of his character.

To begin with that part of him which is least known to you—in shape and stature More is not a tall man, but not remarkably short, all his limbs being so symmetrical that no fault is to be observed in this respect. His complexion is fair, his face rather blond than pale, but with no approach to redness, except for a very delicate flush, which lights up the whole. His head is au-

[1] A famous Greek painter of the fourth century, renowned for the realism of his pictures.

[2] Fulvius and Rutuba appear in Horace's *Satires* (II, vii, 96). Erasmus has taken them to be humble artists, whose rough chalk or charcoal drawings of gladiators in action attracted the attention of the passerby. The usual interpretation of Horace's lines makes Fulvius and Rutuba themselves the gladiators.

burn inclining to black, or if you like it better, black inclining
to auburn; his beard thin, his eyes a bluish gray with a sort of
tinting in them. This kind of eye is thought to be a sign of the
happiest character, and is regarded with favor in England, ·
whereas with us black eyes are preferred. It is said that no kind
of eye is so free from defects of sight. His countenance answers to
his character, having an expression of kind and friendly cheer-
fulness with a little air of raillery. To speak candidly, it is a face
more expressive of pleasantry than of gravity or dignity, though
very far removed from folly or buffoonery. His right shoulder
seems a little higher than his left, especially when he is walking,
a peculiarity that is not innate but the result of habit, like many
tricks of the kind. In the rest of his body there is nothing displeasing,—only his hands are a little coarse, or appear so, as compared with the rest of his figure.

He has always from his boyhood been so negligent of his
toilet as not to give much attention to the things, which according to Ovid [3] are all that men need care about. What a charm
there was in his looks when young, may even now be inferred
from what remains. I knew him myself when he was not more
than three-and-twenty years old; for he has not yet passed much
beyond his fortieth year. His health is sound rather than robust,
but sufficient for any labors suited to an honorable citizen; and
we may fairly hope that his life may be long, as he has a father
living of great age, but an age full of freshness and vigor.

I have never seen any person less fastidious in his choice of

[3] *The Art of Love;* see Book I, 514-522.

food. As a young man, he was by preference a water-drinker, a practice he derived from his father. But not to give annoyance to others, he used at table to conceal this habit from his guests by drinking, out of a pewter vessel, either small beer almost as weak as water, or else plain water. As to wine, it being the custom where he was for the company to invite each other to drink in turn out of the same cup, he used sometimes to sip a little of it, to avoid appearing to shrink from it altogether, and to habituate himself to the common practice. For his eating he has usually preferred beef and salt meats, and household bread, thoroughly fermented, to those articles of diet which are commonly regarded as delicacies. But he does not shrink from things that impart an innocent pleasure, even of a bodily kind, and has always a good appetite for milk-puddings and for fruit, and eats a dish of eggs with the greatest relish.

His voice is neither loud nor excessively low, but of a penetrating tone. It has nothing in it melodious or soft, but is simply suitable for speech, as he does not seem to have any natural talent for singing, though he takes pleasure in music of every kind. His articulation is wonderfully distinct, being equally free from hurry and from hesitation.

He likes to dress simply, and does not wear silk, or purple, or gold chains, except when it is not allowable to dispense with them.[4] He cares marvelously little for those formalities which with ordinary people are the test of politeness; and as he does not exact these ceremonies from others, so he is not scrupulous

[4] See how this trait of More is reflected in the character of the Utopians. See p. 82 and p. 106.

in observing them himself, either on occasions of meeting or at entertainments, though he understands how to use them, if he thinks proper to do so; but he thinks it effeminate and unworthy of a man to waste much time on such trifles.

He was formerly rather disinclined to Court life and to any intimacy with princes, having always a special hatred of tyranny and a great fancy for equality; whereas you will scarcely find any Court so well-ordered as not to have much bustle and ambition and pretense and luxury, or to be free from tyranny in some form or other. He could not even be tempted to Henry the Eighth's Court without great trouble, although no one more courteous or less exacting than this Prince could be desired. He is naturally fond of liberty and leisure; but, as he enjoys a holiday when he has it, so whenever business requires it, no one is more vigilant or more patient.

He seems to be born and made for friendship, of which he is the sincerest and most persistent devotee. Neither is he afraid of that multiplicity of friends, of which Hesiod [5] disapproves. Accessible to every offer of intimacy, he is by no means fastidious in choosing his acquaintances, while he is most accommodating in keeping on with them, and constant in retaining them. If he has fallen in with anyone whose faults he cannot cure, he finds some opportunity of parting with him, untying the knot of intimacy without tearing it; but when he has found sincere friends, whose characters are suited to his own, he is so delighted

[5] See *Works and Days* (II, 707-716) in which Hesiod advises against being on too familiar terms with one's friends, and deems it more valuable to have the constancy of a few than to turn here and there among many.

with their society and conversation, that he seems to see in them the chief pleasure of life, having an absolute distaste for tennis and dice and cards, and the other games with which the mass of gentlemen beguile the tediousness of Time. It should be added that, while he is somewhat neglectful of his own interest, no one takes more pains in attending to the concerns of his friends. What more need I say? If anyone asks for a perfect example of true friendship, it is in More that he will best find it.

In company, his extraordinary kindness and sweetness of temper are such as to cheer the dullest spirit, and lighten the annoyance of the most trying circumstances. From boyhood he was always so pleased with a joke, that it might seem that jesting was the main object of his life; [6] but with all that, he never went to the length of buffoonery, nor had he ever any inclination to bitterness. When quite young, he wrote farces and acted them. A facetious remark charmed him, even though it was aimed at himself, so much did he enjoy any witticism that had a flavor of subtlety or genius. This led to his amusing himself as a young man with epigrams, and taking great delight in Lucian. Indeed, it was he that suggested my writing the *Moria,* or *Praise of Folly,* [7] which was much the same thing as setting a camel to dance.

6 This love of jesting is borne out in Roper's account. See particularly his description of More's last days and his jests with his executioners.

7 This most popular of the writings of Erasmus was written in More's home in 1509, on the third visit of the Dutch scholar to England. It was dedicated to More who was, the author said, "wont to enjoy to the full jokes of this kind." The dedication (See Classics Club edition of *The Praise of Folly,* p. 91) contains a slightly different account of how the book came to be written from that given above, but in both instances, the inspiration for it is attributed to More.

There is no occurence in human life from which he does not seek to extract some pleasure, although the event may be serious in itself. If he has to do with the learned and intelligent, he is delighted with their cleverness, if with unlearned or stupid people, he finds amusement in their folly. He is not offended even by professed clowns, as he adapts himself with marvelous dexterity to the tastes of all; while with ladies generally, and even with his wife, his conversation is made up of humor and playfulness. You would say it was a second Democritus.[8] or rather a Pythagorean philosopher who strolls in leisurely mood through the market place, contemplating the turmoil of those who buy and sell. No one is less swayed by the opinion of the multitude, but on the other hand no one sticks more closely to common sense.

One of his amusements is observing the forms, characters and instincts of different animals. Accordingly there is scarcely any kind of bird that he does not keep about his house; and the same of other animals not quite so common, as monkeys, foxes, ferrets, weasels and the like.[9] Beside these, if he meets with any strange object, imported from abroad or otherwise remarkable, he is eager to buy it. His house is so well supplied with these objects that there is something in every room which catches your eye, as you enter it; and his

[8] Democritus was the Greek philosopher of the late fifth century whose emphasis on the value of good humor in his ethical teaching earned him the title of the "laughing philosopher."

[9] More's pet monkey appears near Lady Alice in Holbein's famous drawing of the More family. It is also renowned as the subject of one of Erasmus' Colloquies.

own pleasure is renewed every time he sees others interested.

When of a sentimental age, he was not a stranger to the emotions of love, but without loss of character, having no inclination to press his advantage, and being more attracted by a mutual liking than by any licentious object.

From his earliest years he drank deep of good letters; and as a young man, he applied himself to the study of Greek and philosophy; but his father was so far from encouraging him in this pursuit, that he withdrew his allowance and almost disowned him, because he thought he was deserting his hereditary calling, being himself an expert professor of English Law.[10] For remote as that profession is from true learning, those who become masters of it have the highest rank and reputation among their countrymen; and it is difficult to find any readier road to fortune and honor. Indeed a considerable part of the nobility of that island had its origin in this profession, in which it is said no one can be perfect, unless he has toiled at it for many years. It was natural that in his younger days our friend's genius, born for better things, should shrink from this study; nevertheless, after he had tasted the learning of the Schools, he became so skilled in it, that there was no one more eagerly consulted by suitors; and the income that he made by it was not surpassed by any of those who did nothing else. Such was the power and quickness of his intellect.

[10] John More, father of Thomas, was trained in the law at Lincoln's Inn, and became in time, a Judge of the King's Bench. Likewise his grandfather, another John More, was a student of the law, and Reader at Lincoln's Inn in 1489-95. Hence the desire to have Thomas carry on the "hereditary calling" was a natural one.

He also spent much labor in reading the volumes of the orthodox Fathers; and when scarcely more than a youth, he lectured publicly on the *De Civitate Dei* [11] of Augustine before a numerous audience. Old priests were not ashamed to take a lesson in divinity from a young layman, and not at all sorry to have done so. Meantime he applied his whole mind to religion, having some thought of taking orders, for which he prepared himself by watchings and fastings and prayers and such like exercises. Therein he showed much more wisdom than the generality of people, who rashly undertake so arduous a profession without testing themselves beforehand. And indeed there was no obstacle to his adopting this kind of life, except the fact that he could not shake off his wish to marry. Accordingly he resolved to be a chaste husband rather than a licentious priest.

When he married, he chose a very young girl, a lady by birth, with her character still unformed, who had been always kept in the country with her parents and sisters,—so that he was all the better able to fashion her according to his own habits. Under his direction she was instructed in learning and in every kind of music, and had almost completely become just such a person as would have been a delightful companion for his whole life, when an early death carried her away.[12]

[11] *The City of God.* These were the lectures More gave at Grocyn's invitation at the church of St. Lawrence Jewry in London. He was then twenty-three years old. See Roper's *Life*, p. 211.

[12] More's first wife was Jane Colt, the daughter of an Essex gentleman, and one of a family of eighteen children. She married More at the age of seventeen and died six years later leaving four children: Margaret, Elizabeth, Cecily, and a son, John More. Erasmus errs in naming Alice as the second daughter. He was

She had however borne him several children, of whom three girls, Margaret, Alice, and Cecily, and one boy, John, are still living.

More did not however long remain single, but contrary to his friends' advice, a few months after his wife's death, he married a widow,[13] more for the sake of the management of his household, than to please his own fancy, as she is no great beauty, nor yet young, as he sometimes laughingly says, but a sharp and watchful housewife. With her nevertheless he lives on as sweet and pleasant terms as if she were as young and lovely as anyone could desire; and scarcely any husband obtains from his wife by masterfulness and severity as much compliance as he does by blandishments and jests. Indeed, what more compliance could he have, when he has induced a woman who is already elderly, who is not naturally of a yielding character, and whose mind is occupied with business, to learn to play the harp, the viol, the spinet and the flute, and to give up every day a prescribed time to practice? With similar kindness he rules his whole household, in which there are no tragic incidents, and no quarrels. If anything of the kind should seem likely to happen, he either calms it down, or at once applies a remedy. And in parting with any

---

apparently thinking of a stepdaughter, the child of More's second wife who later became Lady Alice Alington, and interceded with the Lord Chancellor for her stepfather when More was in the Tower.

13 More's second wife was Alice Middleton, formerly the wife of John Middleton, a London mercer. There were no children by this marriage. Dame Alice was apparently a practical, matter-of-fact person. Other reports support Erasmus' description of her. See Roper's *Life*, p. 266.

member of his household he has never acted in a hostile spirit, or treated him as an enemy. Indeed his house seems to have a sort of charmed felicity, no one having lived in it without being advanced to higher fortune, no inmate having ever had a stain upon his character.

It would be difficult to find any one living on such terms with a mother as he does with his stepmother. For his father has brought in one stepmother after another, and he has been as affectionate with each of them as with a mother. He has lately introduced a third,[14] and More swears that he never liked anything better. His affection for his parents, children and sisters is such that he neither wearies them with his love, nor ever fails in any kindly attention.

His character is entirely free from any touch of avarice. He has set aside out of his property what he thinks sufficient for his children, and spends the rest in a liberal fashion. When he was still dependent on his profession, he gave every client true and friendly counsel with an eye to their advantage rather than to his own, generally advising them that the cheapest thing they could do was to come to terms with their opponents. If he could not persuade them to do this, he pointed out how they might go to law at least expense; for there are people whose character makes them delight in litigation.

In the City of London, where he was born, he acted for some

---

[14] Though old John More admitted that matrimony was a "perilous choice," as if "ye should put your hand into a blind bag full of snakes and eels together, seven snakes for one eel," he was courageous in its practice, and when almost seventy, married a fourth wife.

years as judge in civil cases.[15] This office, which is by no means burdensome—inasmuch as the Court sits only on Thursday before dinner—is considered highly honorable; and no judge ever disposed of more suits, or conducted himself with more perfect integrity. In most cases he remitted the fees which are due from the litigants, though the practice is for the plaintiff to deposit three groats before the hearing, and the defendant a like sum, no more being allowed to be exacted. By such conduct he made himself extremely popular in the City.

He had made up his mind to be contented with this position, which was sufficiently dignified without being exposed to serious dangers. But he had been thrust more than once into an embassy,[16] in the conduct of which he had shown great ability; and King Henry in consequence would never rest until he dragged him to his Court. 'Dragged him,' I say, and with reason; for no one was ever more ambitious to be admitted into a Court than he was anxious to escape it. But as this excellent monarch was resolved to pack his household with learned, serious, intelligent and honest men, he especially insisted upon having More among them and is on such terms of intimacy with him that he cannot bear to let him go. If serious affairs are in hand, no one gives wiser counsel; if it pleases the King to relax his mind with agreeable conversation, no man is better company. Difficult questions are often arising, which require a grave and

[15] More was appointed Under-Sheriff in the City of London, September 3, 1510. In this office he acted as legal adviser to the Mayor and Sheriffs, who were not, as a rule, legally trained. See Roper's account of his success in this office, p. 215.
[16] More's first embassy was to Flanders in 1515 and his second to Calais in 1517.

prudent judge; and these questions are settled by More in such a way that both sides are satisfied. And yet no one has ever induced him to accept a present. What a blessing it would be for the world, if sovereigns everywhere put magistrates like More in office!

Meantime there is no assumption of superiority. In the midst of the great pressure of business he remembers his humble friends, and from time to time returns to his beloved studies. Whatever authority he derives from his rank, and whatever influence he enjoys by the favor of a powerful sovereign, he employs in the service of the public or in that of his friends. It has always been part of his character to be most obliging to everybody, and marvelously ready with his sympathy; and this disposition is more conspicuous than ever, now that his power of doing good is greater. Some he relieves with money, some he protects by his authority, some he promotes by his recommendation, while those whom he cannot otherwise assist he helps by his advice. No one is sent away in distress; you might call him the general patron of all poor people. He counts it a great gain to himself when he relieves an oppressed person, makes the path clear for one in difficulties, or brings back into favor one that was in disgrace. No man more readily confers a benefit, no man expects less in return. And successful as he is in so many ways, though success is generally accompanied by self-conceit, I have never seen any mortal freer from this failing.

I will now turn to the subject of those studies which have been the chief means of bringing More and me together. In early youth his principal compositions were in verse. He afterwards wrestled for a long time to make his prose more smooth; practicing his pen in every kind of writing in order to form that style whose character I do not need to recall, especially to you, who have his books always in your hands. He took the greatest pleasure in speech writing, choosing some arguable subject, as involving a keener exercise of mind. Hence, while still a youth, he attempted a dialogue, in which he maintained a defense of Plato's community, even in the matter of wives! [17] He wrote an answer to Lucian's *Tyrannicide,* in which argument he wished me to be his rival, in order to test his own proficiency in this kind of writing.

He published his *Utopia* for the purpose of showing what things create mischief in commonwealths, having the English constitution especially in view, which he so thoroughly knows and understands. He had written the second book at his leisure; then afterwards, when he found it was required, he added the first off-hand. Hence there is some unevenness in the style.

It would be difficult to find anyone more successful in speaking *extempore.* The happiest thoughts are expressed in the happiest language, while a mind that catches up and anticipates all that is passing, and a ready memory, having everything as it were in stock, promptly supply whatever the time or the occasion demands. In debate no one can be imagined more acute, so that the most eminent theologians often find their match,

[17] See Plato's theory of a community of wives and children in *The Republic,* Book V, Classics Club edition, p. 343.

when he meets them on their own ground. Hence John Colet, a man of keen and exact judgment, is wont to say in familiar conversation that England has only one genius, although the island abounds in distinguished intellects.

However averse he may be to superstition, he is a steady follower of true piety, with regular hours for his prayers, which are uttered not by rote, but from the heart. He talks with his friends about a future life in such a way as to make you feel that he believes what he says, and does not speak without strong hope.

Such is More, even at Court; and there are still people who think that Christians are to be found only in monasteries! Such are the persons whom a wise King admits into his household and into his chamber; and not only admits, but invites, nay, compels to come in.[18] These he has by him as constant witness and judges of his life—as his advisers and traveling companions. By these he rejoices to be accompanied, rather than by dissolute young men or fops, or even by decorated grandees, or crafty ministers, one of whom would lure him to silly amusements, another would incite him to tyranny, and a third would suggest some fresh schemes for plundering his people. If you had lived at this Court, you would, I am sure, give a new description of Court life, and cease to be *Misaulos*.[19] However, you too live with so good a prince that you cannot wish for a better, and have some companions like Stromer and Copp, whose sympathies

[18] The following testimony shows the high regard for Henry VIII felt by humanist scholars in the early years of his reign.
[19] A Court hater.

are on the right side.[20] But what is that small number compared
with such a swarm of distinguished men as Mountjoy, Linacre,
Pace, Colet, Stokesley, Latimer, More, Tunstall, Clerk, and
others like them, any one of whose names signifies at once a
world of virtues and accomplishments? [21] However, I have no
mean hope that Albert, who is at this time the one ornament of
our Germany, will attach to his household a multitude of persons like himself, and set a notable example to other princes; so
that they may exert themselves in their own circles to do the
like.

You have now before you an ill-drawn portrait by a poor
artist of an excellent original! You will be still less pleased with

[20] Hutten's prince was Albert, imperial elector and archbishop of Mainz and of
Magdeburg. He too was a patron of learning. Stromer (Henry Auerbach) and
Copp (Wilhelm Copus) were German humanists and doctors of medicine.
Auerbach was court physician to several German princes including Albert. He
was likewise known as the builder of the famous "Auerbach's Keller" in Leipzig,
famed in connection with the Faust legends. Copus was court physician to
Louis XII and Francis I of France. He translated the medical works of Galen and
Hippocrates and was a friend of both Hutten and Erasmus.

[21] These men were all familiar figures at the court of Henry VIII. More speaks
of Tunstall in the first paragraph of the *Utopia* (see p. 15); and the names of
Linacre, Colet, and Latimer are well known. Lord Mountjoy as a youth had
studied under Erasmus on the Continent and was instrumental in arranging
for his first visit to England. He was one of Henry's wealthiest courtiers. Richard
Pace became the King's secretary of state in 1516, and served both him and
Wolsey in important missions abroad. With More he was influential in estab-
lishing chairs of Greek at both Cambridge and Oxford. John Stokesley was the
King's chaplain early in his reign, and later a privy councilor. He wrote in
favor of the King's divorce, but opposed any changes in church doctrine. John
Clerk, later bishop of Bath and Wells, was trained in law at Bologna and
served Wolsey as chaplain and adviser. It was Clerk who in 1521, presented the
Pope with the King's book against Luther.

the portrait, if you come to have a closer acquaintance with More himself. But meantime I have made sure of this, that you cannot charge me with ignoring your command, nor continue to find fault with the shortness of my letters; though even this one has not seemed long to me in writing it, and will not, I am confident, appear prolix to you, as you read it. Our More's sweetness will ensure that.

Further—not to leave unanswered your last letter, which I read in print before I saw it in writing,—I have been informed of the kindness of the most illustrious Prince Albert by his letter to me. But how, I should like to know, has it come to pass, that the cup reached everyone by means of your letter before it has come to me? [22] You certainly could not have sent it more safely by anyone than by Richard Pace, the ambassador of the English king, whether I was in Brabant or in England.

You, I see, are doing vigorous battle both with the pen and with the sword—successfully too, as well as bravely! For I hear you are in great favor with the Cardinal of Gaëta.[23] I am glad that we have good news of *Capnio*.[24] If Literature allows the

[22] Erasmus received gifts from people all over western Europe, varying in kind and quality from large sums of money to a bag of sweetmeats. Apparently Prince Albert was sending him a cup.

[23] Tommaso de Vio, or Cardinal Cajetan, as he was better known, was an Italian churchman and scholar. He was sent into Germany in 1518 to quiet the trouble aroused by Luther, and in 1519 conducted the tribunal at Augsburg before which Luther was called. He was a moderate reformer and sought to reconcile the best elements of humanistic thought with the best elements of orthodox Catholicism.

[24] Capnio was a name for the great German humanist Reuchlin. He had for years been engaged in a struggle against the Dominicans, who attempted to construe his defense of Hebrew literature as heresy. Franz von Sickingen, a friend of

name of **Franz** von Sickingen to die, she may fairly be taxed with ingratitude.

For our own news, there will be another occasion to speak of it. Only this at present: business is conducted at this Court by the meanest sycophancy—an art to which I must confess myself unequal. If there is anyone of your acquaintance who wants to learn it, I will point him out a wonderful master of this accomplishment—one, of whom you may say that he was palpably born for it. Cicero was not a more successful orator than he is a sycophant; and he finds many docile pupils among us! The right time is not come, but before long I will introduce him to you, so that he may obtain the glory which he well deserves, and of which he is sadly ambitious. He will then be celebrated in the letters of all the learned, but as a portent rather than a man. Farewell.

Antwerp, 23 July.

Hutten and later a leader of a patriotic movement of the German knights, threw his weight in favor of Reuchlin in the above struggle. Erasmus may have been thinking of this in the sentence that follows.

ROPER'S LIFE OF MORE

ROPER'S LIFE OF MORE

By far the best known and by many the best loved biography of Thomas More is that written by his son-in-law, William Roper. Roper was one of several young people who lived in More's genial household when the More children were growing up. Exactly when he joined the group is not known, but it was probably in 1518, when he became a law student at Lincoln's Inn. Three years later he married Margaret, More's eldest daughter, and they continued to be members of the household. According to Roper's own account, he was resident there "by the space of sixteen years and more."

In addition to holding various offices for which his legal training had fitted him, young Roper was a member of the House of Commons during some of the years that witnessed Parliament's handling of events closely touching the life and career of More. Hence he was eminently suited to know both the public and private life of his famous father-in-law. In spite of this close relationship, the biography is not a document for the historian who seeks a chronological account of More's career, with all names and dates correct, as the numerous footnotes here added will show.

Roper himself made no pretentious claims for his work, saying simply, "I . . . thought it, therefore, my part to set forth such matters touching his life as I could at this present remember. . . ." He was writing some twenty years after the latest events which he records. And he was not, moreover, an eyewitness to all the scenes he describes, nor the auditor of all the conversations he reports. But one does not live for sixteen years in a household without knowing it pretty well. And if the conversations which Roper presents as having passed between himself and More, or the words he puts into the mouths of Dame Alice or his wife Meg are not the words actually spoken, it is yet likely that they are veracious in tone and spirit.

The fame of the biography has increased rather than diminished with time. It was not published until almost a century after the events which it describes had occurred. It appeared first in 1626, according to its title page, in Paris. But the manuscript had already been used by early biographers of More. Several new editions appeared in the eighteenth century, and it has been re-edited from time to time since. Four manuscript copies are extant, two at least in the handwriting of Roper's own day, and may be seen in the British Museum. To students of the Elizabethan period, the *Life* is not only a memento of More, but of the age in which he lived.

THE LIFE OF SIR THOMAS MORE

by William Roper

FORASMUCH as Sir Thomas More, Knight, sometime
Lord Chancellor of England, a man of singular virtue and
clear unspotted conscience, as Erasmus [1] witnesses, more pure
and white than the whitest snow, and of such an angelical wit,
as England, he says, never had the like before, nor ever shall
again, who was universally as well versed in the laws of our
realm (a study, in effect, able to occupy the whole life of a man)
as in all other sciences, was in his days accounted a man worthy
of fame and memory; I, William Roper (though most unworthy), his son-in-law by marriage with his eldest daughter,
knowing that no one man understood so much of him and of
his doings as myself, since I was continually resident in his
house for the space of sixteen years and more, have thought it
therefore my part to set forth such matters touching his life as
I could at this present call to remembrance. Among which, very
many notable things, which should have been remembered, have
through negligence and long continuance of time slipped out of
my mind. Yet to the intent that the same shall not all utterly
perish, I have at the desire of divers worshipful friends of mine,

[1] See letter from Erasmus, p. 187.

though very far from the grace and worthiness of them, as far forth as my meager wit, memory, and learning would serve me, declared as much thereof as in my poor judgment seemed worthy to be remembered.

This Sir Thomas More after he had been brought up in the Latin tongue at St. Anthony's [2] in London, was, by his father's procurement received into the house of the right reverend, wise and learned prelate Cardinal Morton.[3] Here, though he was young of years, yet would he at Christmastide suddenly sometimes step in among the players, and never studying for the matter, make a part of his own there presently among them, which made the lookers-on more sport than all the players beside. In whose wit and forwardness the Cardinal much delighting would often say of him to the nobles that divers time dined with him: "This child here waiting at the table, whosoever shall live to see it, will prove a marvelous man."

Whereupon for his learning he placed him at Oxford, whence, when he was both in the Greek and Latin tongue sufficiently instructed, he was for the study of the law of the realm put to an Inn of the Chancery, called New Inn, where for the time, he very well prospered. And from thence he was committed to

[2] St. Anthony's school in Threadneedle Street was more than two centuries old at the time More attended it. Contemporaries described it as the leading school in London until John Colet founded St. Paul's in 1512.

[3] It was customary for the sons of good families to be placed in the homes of noblemen and ranking churchmen where they would learn good manners and the conduct of a gentleman. Young Thomas More was highly privileged; for Thomas Morton was already Archbishop of Canterbury and Lord Chancellor, and was soon to become Cardinal Morton, as Roper describes him.

Lincoln's Inn, with very small allowance, continuing there his study until he was made and accounted a worthy utter barrister.[4] After this, to his great commendation, he for some time gave public lectures on St. Augustine's *De Civitate Dei* [5] in the church of St. Laurence in the Old Jewry, whereunto there resorted Doctor Grocyn, an excellent wise man, and all the chief learned men of the City of London. Then he was made Reader of Furnival's Inn, remaining there for the space of three years and more.

After which time he gave himself to devotion and prayer in the Charterhouse of London,[6] religiously living there without vow about four years, until he resorted to the house of one Mr. Colt, a gentleman of Essex, that had often invited him thither, having three daughters whose honest conversation and virtuous education provoked him there especially to set his affection. And albeit his mind most inclined him to the second daughter, for he thought her the fairest and best favored, yet when he considered that it would be both great grief and some shame also to the eldest to see her younger sister preferred in marriage before her, he then of a certain pity framed his fancy towards

[4] Utter barristers were those students at the Inns of Court who ranked next to the readers. The readers, or benchers, were the senior members. The various Inns mentioned were schools and associations for judges, lawyers, and law students in London.

[5] *The City of God,* the great theological and historical treatise by St. Augustine, Bishop of Hippo.

[6] Charterhouse, now moved from London into Surrey, is best known as one of England's famous public schools. But when the above was written, Charterhouse was still the house of an order of Carthusian monks. Lay scholars might live there for a time under monastic regulations without taking vows.

her, and soon after married her, nevertheless not discontinuing his study of the law at Lincoln's Inn, but applying still the same, until he was called to the Bench, and had read twice, which is as often as any judge of the law does read. Before which time he had placed himself and his wife at Bucklesbury in London, where he had by her three daughters, brought up from their youth in virtue and learning, whom he would often exhort to take virtue and learning for their meat, and play but for their sauce.

But ere ever he became reader in Court he was, in the latter part of King Henry the Seventh's reign, made a Burgess in the Parliament wherein there were by the King demanded, as I have heard it reported, about three-fifteenths [7] for the marriage of his eldest daughter, who was to be the Scottish queen. At the last debate on this, he made such arguments and reasons there against it that the King's demands were thereupon rejected. So that one of the King's privy chamber named Mr. Tyler, being present thereat, brought word to the King out of Parliament house that a beardless boy had disappointed all his purposes. Whereupon the King, conceiving great indignation towards him, could not be satisfied until he had some way avenged it. And forasmuch as the young man having nothing, could lose nothing, his Grace devised a causeless quarrel against his father, keeping him in the Tower until he had paid him a hundred pounds fine.

Shortly hereupon it happened that this Sir Thomas More came

[7] A "fifteenth" was a tax or subsidy made by grant of Parliament to the King, and exacted from all property holders.

in a suit to Dr. Fox, Bishop of Winchester, one of the King's Privy Council. The Bishop called him aside, and pretending great favor towards him, promised him that if he would be ruled by him, he would not fail to restore him into the King's favor again, meaning, as it was afterward conjectured, to cause him thereby to confess his offense against the King, whereby his Highness might with better excuse have occasion to avenge his displeasure against him. But as he came from the Bishop, he fell into conversation with one Mr. Witford, his familiar friend, then chaplain to that Bishop, and afterward a Father of Sion,[8] and told him what the Bishop had said to him, desiring to have his advice therein; who, for the passion of God, prayed him in no wise to follow the Bishop's counsel. "For my Lord Bishop, my master," quoth he, "in order to serve the King's turn, would agree to his own father's death." So Sir Thomas More returned to the Bishop no more. And had not the King soon after died, he was determined to have gone over the sea, thinking that being in the King's indignation he could not live in England without great danger.

Afterward he was made one of the under-sheriffs of London, by which office and his learning together, as I have heard him say, he gained with no great effort more than four hundred pounds by the year; since there was at that time in none of the

---

[8] Sion, the famous convent at Isleworth on the Thames, was a house of the celebrated order of St. Bridget of Sweden. Attached to each convent of the Brigittines, as they were called, was a small community of monastic clergy who acted as chaplains for the order. Mr. Witford to whom Roper refers was apparently one of these.

Prince's courts of the laws of this realm any matter of importance in controversy wherein he was not a counselor of one party. Whom, for his learning, wisdom, and knowledge and experience, men held in such estimation that before he came into the service of King Henry the Eighth, he was, at the request of the English Merchants, by the King's consent, made twice ambassador in certain great cases between them and the Merchants of the Stilliard.[9] His wise and discreet dealing therein, to his high commendation, coming to the King's attention, led his Highness to cause Cardinal Wolsey, then Lord Chancellor, to procure him for his service. And albeit the Cardinal according to the King's request labored with him to that end, among many other persuasions alleging to him how dear his service must needs be unto his Majesty, who could not with honor recompense him with less than he should yearly lose thereby; yet he, loth to change his estate, gave such reasons to the King by the Cardinal to the contrary, that his Grace for that time was well satisfied.

Now there happened after this a great ship of the Pope to arrive at Southampton, which the King claiming for a forfeiture, the Pope's Ambassador obtained by suit unto his Grace that he might for his Master the Pope have counsel learned in the laws of this realm; and that the matter might in his own presence

[9] The "Steelyard" was the London center for the German merchants, members of the Hanseatic League. They formed a small colony and were granted many special privileges. The "English Merchants" were the company of Merchant Adventurers. Roper is wrong in assigning More's second embassy also to matters between the English merchants and those of the Steelyard. His second was to Calais to negotiate with French merchants, not those of the Hanse.

(being himself only a civilian) be openly heard and discussed in some public place. At which time there could none of our lawyers be found so suited to be counselor to this Ambassador as Sir Thomas More, who could report to the Ambassador in Latin all the reasons and arguments alleged by the learned counsel on both sides. Upon this the Chancellor, and other judges in the Star Chamber, had audience accordingly. Where Sir Thomas More not only declared to the Ambassador the whole substance of all their opinions, but also argued so learnedly himself in defense on the Pope's side, that the aforesaid forfeiture to the Pope was restored, and himself was so greatly renowned among all the hearers for his upright and commendable demeanor therein, that for no entreaty would the King from henceforth be induced any longer to do without his service. At his first entry thereunto he made him Master of the Requests,[10] having then no better place vacant, and within a month after, a Knight and one of his Privy Council.

And so from time to time he was by the Prince advanced, continuing in his singular favor and trusty service twenty years and above, during a good part whereof the King upon holidays, when he had done his own devotions, used to send for him into his private room, and there sometimes on matters of Astronomy, Geometry, Divinity, and such other Faculties, and sometimes on his worldly affairs, would sit and confer with him, and at other times would he in the night have him up on

[10] Roper's memory has played him false, as More was made a member of the King's Council and a judge in the Court of Requests, or Poor Man's Court as it was commonly called, in 1517. He was not knighted until 1521.

the roof, there to consider with him the diversities, courses, motions, and operations of the stars and planets. And because he was of a pleasant disposition, it pleased the King and Queen, after the Council had supped, at the time of their supper for their pleasure commonly to call for him to be merry with them. When he perceived that the King so much delighted in his talk that he could not once in a month get leave to go home to his wife and children (whose company he most desired) and that he could not be absent from the Court two days together without being thither sent for again, he, much disliking this restraint of liberty, began thereupon somewhat to dissemble his nature, and so little by little to desist from his former mirth so that he was thenceforth no more than ordinarily sent for by them. Then died one Mr. Weston, Treasurer of the Exchequer, whose office after his death the King by his own offer, without any asking, freely gave unto Sir Thomas More.[11]

In the fourteenth year of his Grace's reign, there was a Parliament held, wherein Sir Thomas More was chosen Speaker, who being very loth to take that office upon him, made an oration, not now extant, to the King's Highness to be relieved therefrom. Whereunto, when the King would not consent, he spake unto his Grace in form following: "Since I perceive, most redoubtable sovereign, that it stands not with your Highness' pleasure to undo this election, and cause it to be changed, but you have

[11] Roper's account is here again in conflict with the official records. More was made an Under-Treasurer, not a Treasurer of the Exchequer, and his predecessor in the office was Sir John Cutte rather than Weston, who came to the office later and lived some twenty years beyond the date ascribed to him by Roper.

by the mouth of the Right Reverend Father in God the Legate, your Highness' Chancellor, given thereto your most royal consent, and have by your benignity determined, far above what I deserve, to empower me, and for this office to declare me fit; rather than that you should seem to impute unto your Commons that they had unsuitably chosen, I am therefore, and always shall be, ready obediently to conform myself to the accomplishment of your high commandment. In my most humble wise beseeching your most noble Majesty, that I may, with your Grace's favor, before I enter farther into it, make my humble intercession into your Highness for two lowly petitions, the one privately concerning myself, the other, the whole assembly of your House of Commons. And for myself, gracious Sovereign, that if I should have the misfortune in anything hereafter, which is to be declared on behalf of your Commons in your high presence, to mistake my message, or for lack of good utterance in presenting it to pervert or impair their prudent instructions, you will then, most noble Majesty, by your abundant grace, and with the eye of your accustomed pity, pardon my simplicity, giving me leave again to repair to the House of Commons, and there to confer with them, and to take their substantial advice, what thing, and in what wise I shall on their behalf utter and speak before your noble Grace; to the intent that their prudent recommendations and affairs be not by my simpleness and folly hindered or impaired. Which thing, if it should so happen, as it were well likely to happen with me (if your Grace's benignity relieved not my oversight), it could not fail to be, during my life, a perpetual regret and heaviness to my heart.

The help and remedy whereof in manner aforesaid is, most gracious Sovereign, my first lowly suit and humble petition unto your most noble Grace.

"My other humble request, most excellent Prince, is this. Forasmuch as there are of your Commons here, by your high commandment, assembled for your parliament, a great number who are, after the accustomed manner, appointed in the House of Commons to treat and advise of the common affairs among themselves apart; and albeit, my liege Lord, that, according to your prudent advice, by your honorable writs everywhere declared, there has been as due diligence used in sending up to your Highness' Court of Parliament the most discreet persons out of every quarter as men could esteem fit thereto; wherefore it is not to be doubted but that there is a very substantial assembly of right wise and politic persons: yet, most victorious Prince, since among so many wise men, neither is every man equally wise, nor among so many men, equally well witted or well spoken; and it often happens likewise that much folly is uttered in painted polished speeches, and that many who are boisterous and rude in language, see deeply indeed, and give right substantial counsel: and since also in matters of great importance the mind is often so occupied with the matter that a man rather studies what to say than how; by reason whereof the wisest man and best spoken in a country happens on occasion while his mind is fervent on a matter, to speak in such wise as he would afterward wish not to have done, and would so gladly change: therefore, most gracious Sovereign, considering that in all your high Courts of Parliament there is nothing treated but matters of weight and importance concerning your realm, and your own royal estate, it could not fail to hinder and put to silence from giving their advice many of your discreet Commons, unless they were utterly relieved of all doubt and fear how anything they should happen to speak should by your Highness be taken: and on this point your well-known benignity puts every man in right good hope.

"And such is the weight of the matter, such is the reverend dread that the timorous hearts of your natural subjects conceive towards your high Majesty, our most redoubted King and undoubted Sovereign, that they cannot on this point find themselves satisfied, unless your gracious bounty banish the scruple of their timorous minds, and animate and encourage them clear of doubt. It may therefore please your most abundant Grace, our most gracious King, to give to all your Commons here assembled, your most gracious licence and pardon freely, without doubt of your dreadful displeasure, for every man to discharge his conscience, and boldly in everything incident among them to declare his advice; and whatsoever any man happens to say, it may please your noble Majesty in your inestimable goodness to take all in good part, interpreting every man's words, how unskillfully soever they be couched, to proceed of good zeal towards the profit of your realm and honor of your royal person, the prosperous estate and preservation whereof, most excellent Sovereign, is the thing which we all, your most humble and loving subjects, according to the most bounden duty of our natural allegiance, most highly desire and pray for."

At this Parliament, Cardinal Wolsey found himself much

vexed with the Burgesses thereof, because nothing was done or spoken therein but it was immediately blown abroad in every alehouse. It so happened at that Parliament that a very great subsidy was demanded, the Cardinal fearing it would not pass the House of Commons, determined for the furtherance thereof, to be present there himself; whereupon before his coming, there was long debating whether it were better to receive him there amongst them, with but a few of his Lords (as the major opinion of the House was) or, royally with a whole train. "Masters," quoth Sir Thomas More, "forasmuch as my Lord Cardinal lately, you note well, laid to our charge a lightness of tongue for things uttered out of this house, it shall not be amiss in my mind to receive him with all his pomp, with his maces, his pillars, his pollaxes, his crosses, his hat, and great seal too; to the intent that if he find the like fault with us hereafter, we may be the bolder ourselves to lay the blame on those his Grace brings with him."

Whereto the House wholly agreeing, he was received accordingly. Where, after he had in a solemn oration by many reasons proved how necessary it was that the demands there moved be granted, and had further said that less would not serve the King's purpose, seeing the company still silent and answering nothing thereto, and contrary to his expectation showing in themselves no readiness of inclination towards his requests, he said to them: "Masters, ye have many wise and learned men among you, and seeing I am from the King's own person sent hither unto you for the preservation of yourselves and all the realm, I think it meet you give me a reasonable answer."

Whereat, every man holding his peace, then he began to speak to one Mr. Marney, who making him no answer either, he asked the same question separately of divers others accounted the wisest of the company.

To whom, when none of them all would give so much as one word, having before agreed, as the custom was, only by their speaker to make answer: "Masters," quoth the Cardinal, "unless it is the manner of your House, as of likelihood it is, in such cases to utter your minds by the mouth of your Speaker, whom ye have chosen because he is trusty and wise, as indeed he is, here is without doubt a marvelous obstinate silence." And thereupon he required the answer of Mr. Speaker, who reverently upon his knees excused the silence of the House, as abashed at the presence of so noble a personage, that was able to amaze the wisest and best learned in the realm, and by many reasons proved that for them to make answer was neither expedient nor in accord with the ancient liberty of the House. In conclusion, for himself he showed, that though they had all trusted him with their voices, yet except every one of them could put into his head all their several wits, he alone in so weighty a matter was unfit to make answer to his Grace. Thereupon the Cardinal, displeased with Sir Thomas More, who had not in this Parliament in all things satisfied his desire, suddenly arose and departed; and after the Parliament ended, uttered unto him all his annoyance, saying, "Would to God you had been at Rome, Mr. More, when I made you Speaker!" "Your Grace not offended, so would I too, my Lord," quoth he, and to put such quarrels out of the Cardinal's head, he began to talk of the gallery at Hampton Court,[12] wherewith he so wisely broke off the Cardinal's unpleasant talk that the Cardinal for the moment, it seemed, knew not what more to say to him.

But for avenging his displeasure he counseled the King to send Sir Thomas More as Ambassador to Spain, commending unto his Highness his wisdom, learning, and fitness for that voyage, saying that considering the difficulty of the cause, none was so well able to serve his Grace therein. When the King had broken this to Sir Thomas More, he declared unto his Grace how unfit a journey it was for him, the nature of the country and the disposition of his complexion [13] so disagreeing that he would never be likely to do his Grace acceptable service therein, knowing right well that if his Grace sent him thither, he would send him to his grave; but showing himself nevertheless ready according to his duty, albeit with the loss of his life, to fulfill his Grace's pleasure therein. The King allowing well his answer, said unto him: "It is not our meaning, Mr. More, to do you hurt, but to do you good we would be glad. We therefore for this purpose will devise some other plan, and employ your service otherwise." And such entire favor did the King bear him that he made him Chancellor of the Duchy of Lancaster, upon the

[12] Wolsey had erected the palace at Hampton Court, one of the best specimens of Tudor architecture now extant. Henry VIII coveted it, and after Wolsey gave it to him, it became his favorite residence.

[13] "Complexion" here means the physical constitution, the "habit of the body," conceived by medieval physiology to be the result of the combination of the four bodily humors. If the combination were in proper proportions, health and "good humor" were the result; if improperly proportioned, ill health and "ill humor" would ensue.

death of Sir Richard Winfield, who had that office before. And for the pleasure he took in his company, his Grace would suddenly sometimes come home to his house at Chelsea to be merry with him; whither once, unlooked for, he came to dinner, and after dinner in a fair garden of his walked with him for the space of an hour, holding his arm about his neck.

As soon as his Grace was gone, I rejoicing told Sir Thomas More how fortunate he was whom the King had so familiarly treated, as I had never seen him do to anyone before, except Cardinal Wolsey, whom I saw his Grace once walk with arm in arm. "I thank our Lord, son," quoth he; "I find his Grace my very good Lord indeed, and I do believe he does as singularly favor me as any subject within this realm. Howbeit, son Roper, I may tell thee, I have no cause to be proud thereof. For if my head would win him a castle in France"—for then there was war between us [14]—"it should not fail to go."

This Sir Thomas More, among all his other virtues, was of such meekness that if it befell that any learned man resorting to him from Oxford, Cambridge, or elsewhere (as there did divers, some for the desire of his acquaintance, some for the famous report of his learning and wisdom, and some for suits of the University) entered into argument, wherein few were comparable to him, and so far discoursed with him that he perceived they could not, without some inconvenience, hold out much further in their disputation against him; then, lest he should discomfit them, since he sought not his own glory, but would

[14] Henry VIII had allied himself in 1522 with the Emperor Charles V of Spain in a war against France.

rather appear conquered than discourage students in their studies, ever showing himself more desirous to learn than to teach, he would by some witty device courteously break off into some other matter and give over.

The King bad such an opinion of his wisdom and learning that at such time as he attended upon his Highness, taking his progress either to Oxford or Cambridge, where he was received with very eloquent orations, his Grace would always assign him, as one that was most prompt and ready therein, *extempore* to make answer thereunto; though the King's manner was, whensoever he had any occasion either here or beyond the sea to be in any University not only to be present at the reading and disputations there commonly used, but also learnedly to dispute among them himself. As Chancellor of the Duchy,[15] Sir Thomas More was made ambassador twice, joined in commission with Cardinal Wolsey, once to the Emperor Charles in Flanders, the other time to the French King in France.

Not long after this the Water Bailiff [16] of London, at one time his servant, hearing, where he had been at dinner, certain merchants railing at length against his old master, waxed so discontented therewith that he hastily came to him and told him what he had heard; "and were I, sir," quoth he, "in such favor and authority with my Prince as you are, such men would

15 This is another error in Roper's chronology. More went as ambassador to Charles in 1521. He did not become Chancellor of the Duchy of Lancaster until 1525.

16 The Water Bailiff of London was one of the four gentlemen who attended the Lord Mayor, the others being the Sword Bearer, the Common Crier, and the Common Hunt.

surely not be permitted so villainously and falsely to mis-report and slander me. Wherefore, I wish you to call them before you, and, to their shame for their lewd malice, punish them."

But Sir Thomas More, smiling upon him, said: "Mr. Water Bailiff, would you have me punish them by whom I receive more benefit than by you all who are my friends? Let them in God's name speak as lewdly as they wish of me, and shoot ever so many arrows at me; so long as they do not hit me, what am I the worse? But if they should once hit me, then would it trouble me a little; howbeit, I trust, by God's help, there shall none of them all be able once to touch me. I have more cause, Mr. Water Bailiff, I assure thee, to pity them than to be angry with them." Such fruitful conversation had he oftentimes with his familiar friends.

So once upon a time walking along the Thames side with me at Chelsea, in talking of other things, he said to me, "Now would to God, son Roper, upon condition that three things were well established in Christendom, I were put in a sack, and here this moment cast into the Thames!" "What great things are these, sir," quoth I, "that should move you so to wish?" "Wouldst thou know, son Roper, what they are?" quoth he. "Yea, truly, sir, with a good will, if it please you," quoth I.

"In faith, they are these, son," quoth he. "The first is, that whereas most of the Christian princes are at mortal wars, that they were at universal peace. The second, that where the Church of Christ is at this present sore afflicted with many heresies and errors, it were well settled in a uniformity of religion. The third, that where the King's matter of his marriage is now come into question, it were, to the glory of God and quietness of all parties, brought to a good conclusion." Whereby, as I could gather, he judged that otherwise it would be a disturbance to a great part of Christendom. Thus did it by his doings throughout the whole course of his life appear that all his travails and pains, without respect of earthly comforts, either to himself or any of his, were wholly bestowed and employed only in the service of God, the Prince, and the realm. In his latter time, I heard it said that he never asked of the King for himself the value of one penny.

Sir Thomas More's daily custom was, if he were at home, besides his private prayers with his children, to say the seven psalms, litany, and suffrages following. It was also his habit nightly, before he went to bed, to go to his chapel with his wife, children, and household, and there upon his knees ordinarily to say certain psalms and collects with them. And because he was desirous for goodly purposes at times to be solitary and sequester himself from worldly company, a good distance from his mansion house he built a place called the new building, wherein was a chapel, a library, and a gallery in which as his use was upon other days to occupy himself in prayer and study together, on Fridays there he usually continued from morning to evening, spending his time duly in devout prayers and spiritual exercises. And to arouse his wife and children to the desire of heavenly things, he would sometimes use these words to them: "It is now no merit for you children to go to heaven. For everybody gives you good counsel, everybody gives you good example. You see virtue rewarded, and vice punished, so that you are carried up to heaven even by the chins. But if you ever live in a time that no man will give you good counsel, no man will give you good example, when you see virtue punished and vice rewarded, if you will then stand fast, and firmly stick to God on pain of death, if you are but half good, God will allow you for whole good."

If his wife or any of his children had been diseased or troubled, he would say to them, "We may not look to go to heaven at our pleasure in feather beds; it is not the way. For our Lord himself went thither with great pain, and by many tribulations, which is the path wherein he walked thither, and the servant may not expect to be in a better condition than his Master." And he would in this sort persuade them to take their troubles patiently, so would he in like manner withstand the devil and his temptations valiantly, saying, "Whoever will mark the devil and his temptations shall find him therein much like an ape. For as an ape not well watched will be busy and bold doing shrewd tricks, and contrariwise, being spied upon, will quickly leap back and adventure no farther; so the devil, seeing a man idle, slothful, and without resistance, ready to receive his temptations, waxes so hardy that he will not fail to continue with him until he has brought him to his purpose. But, on the other hand, if he see a man with diligence ready to prevent and withstand his temptations, he waxes so weary that finally he forsakes him; for the devil by disposition is a spirit of nature so envious that he fears any more to assault him, lest he should thereby not only catch a foul fall himself, but also furnish the man with more ground for merit." Thus delighted Sir Thomas More not only to be occupied himself in virtuous exercises, but also to exhort his wife and children and household to embrace and follow the same.

And to him, because of his notable virtue and godliness, God showed, as it seemed, a manifest miraculous token of his special favor. At that time my wife, as many others that year were, was sick of the sweating sickness,[17] and lying in so great extremity of that disease that by no invention or devices that physicians in such cases commonly use (of whom she had divers, both expert, wise, and well learned, then continually attendant upon her) could she be kept from sleep; so that both the physicians and all the others despaired of her health and recovery, and gave her over. Her father, who took almost entire care of her, being in no small heaviness for her, by prayer sought at God's hands to get remedy; whereupon after his usual manner, going up into his new lodging, there in his chapel upon his knees with tears he most devoutly besought Almighty God that it would be like his goodness, unto whom nothing was impossible, if it were his blessed will, at his mediation, to vouchsafe graciously to hear his petition. There straightway it came into his mind that a clyster would be the one way to help her, which

17 An infectious disease with a high fatality rate, which struck England in epidemic form on five occasions in the fifteenth and sixteenth centuries, but apparently not after that time. It was distinct from "the plague," that is, the bubonic plague, which ravaged the country at intervals; it ran its course quickly, usually within twelve to twenty-four hours. The third visitation, in 1517, struck Oxford and Cambridge with particular severity, and the fourth, in 1528, was especially bad in London and at King Henry's court. Roper's wife, it will be remembered, was More's beloved daughter, Margaret.

when he had told the physicians, they at once confessed that if there were any hope of health, it was the very best help indeed, much marveling among themselves that they had not afore remembered it. Then it was immediately ministered unto her sleeping, which she could by no means have been brought to had she been awake, and albeit after she was thereby thoroughly awaked, God's marks, undoubted token of death, plainly appeared upon her; yet, contrary to all their expectations, she was, as it was thought, by her father's fervent prayer miraculously recovered, and at length restored again to perfect health: whom if it had pleased God at that time to have taken her to his mercy, her father said he would never have meddled with worldly matters again.

Now while Sir Thomas More was Chancellor of the Duchy, the See of Rome chanced to be vacant,[18] which was the cause of much trouble. For Cardinal Wolsey, a man very ambitious, and desirous (as good hope and likelihood he had) to aspire unto that dignity, saw himself disappointed in his expectations, because the Emperor Charles, at the time of the election so highly commended to the Cardinals of Rome one Cardinal Adrian, his one-time schoolmaster, for his virtue and worthiness, that thereupon he was chosen Pope. He came from Spain, where he was then resident, on foot to Rome, and before his entry into that city, put off his hose and shoes and passed barefooted and barelegged through the streets towards his palace with such humbleness that all the people held him in great reverence.

---

[18] Another error in chronology. Adrian was elected Pope in 1522. More was Chancellor of the Duchy of Lancaster 1525-29.

Cardinal Wolsey waxed so angry therewith that he studied to invent all ways of avenging his grief against the Emperor, which, as it was the beginning of a lamentable tragedy, some part whereof is not unconnected with my present purpose, I reckoned requisite here to put in remembrance.

This Cardinal therefore, not ignorant of the King's unconstant and mutable disposition, which soon inclined him to withdraw his devotion from his own most noble and virtuous wife Queen Katherine, aunt to the Emperor, and upon every light occasion to fix his affection upon another, beneath her in nobility, wisdom, virtue, favor, and beauty, and meaning to make his light disposition an instrument to bring about his ungodly intent, devised to allure the King (then already contrary to the Cardinal's desires and expectations falling in love with the Lady Anne Bullen) to cast his fancy to one of the French King's sisters.[19] This thing, because of the enmity and war at that time between the French King and the Emperor (against whom, for the cause afore-mentioned, he was mortally resentful) he was desirous to procure, and for the better achieving thereof he requested Langland, Bishop of Lincoln, and ghostly father [20] to the King, to put a scruple into the King's head that it was not lawful for him to marry his brother's wife.

This the King, not sorry to hear of, spoke of first to Sir Thomas More, whose counsel he required therein, showing him certain places of Scripture that somewhat seemed to serve

[19] It was Renée, the daughter of Louis XII, not a sister of Francis I, whom Wolsey wished Henry to "cast his fancy to."
[20] The King's confessor.

his appetite, which when Sir Thomas had perused, he thereupon, as one that never had professed the study of Divinity,
excused himself, claiming to be unfitted in many ways to meddle
with such matters. The King, not satisfied with this answer, so
strongly still pressed upon him that therefore in conclusion he
consented to permit his Grace his motion; and further, since the
matter was of such importance as needed good advice and
deliberation, he besought his Grace with sufficient respect ad-
visedly to consider it. Wherewith the King, well contented, said
unto him that Tunstall and Clarke, Bishops of Durham and
Bath, with other learned members of his Privy Council, should
also be councilors therein.

So Sir Thomas More, departing, compared those places of
Scripture with the expositions of divers of the old holy doctors,
and at his coming to the Court, in talking with his Grace of the
aforesaid matter, he said: "To be plain with your Grace, neither
my Lord of Durham nor my Lord of Bath, though I know them
both to be wise, virtuous, and learned and honorable prelates,
nor myself with the rest of your Council, being all your Grace's
own servants, for your manifold benefits daily bestowed on us,
so most bounden unto you, are in my judgment fit councilors
for your Grace herein; but if your Grace has a mind to understand the truth, you may choose such councilors as neither for
respect of their own worldly convenience, nor for fear of your
princely authority, will be inclined to deceive you."

Then he named to him St. Jerome, St. Augustine, and divers
other holy doctors, both Greeks and Latins; and moreover
showed him what authority he had gathered out of them;

which, although the King did not very well like (as it was disagreeable to his Grace's desire), yet were they so wisely tempered by Sir Thomas More, who in all his conversation with the King on that matter had always most wisely behaved himself, that he both presently took them in good part, and oftentimes had thereof conference with him again.

After this, certain questions were proposed among his Council —whether the King needed in this case to have any scruple at all, and if he had, what way were best to free him of it. Most of them were of the opinion that there was a good case, and that, for deciding it, suit should be made to the See of Rome, where the King hoped by liberality to obtain his purpose, wherein, as it after appeared, he was far deceived. Then there was for the trial and examination of this matrimony a Commission procured from Rome, on which Cardinal Campeggio and Cardinal Wolsey were joined as Commissioners, who, for the determination thereof, sat at the Blackfriars in London. Where a statement was put in for admitting the said matrimony, alleging the previous marriage between the King and the Queen to be unlawful. But for proof of the marriage to be lawful, there was brought in a dispensation in which after divers disputations held thereon, there appeared an imperfection, which by an instrument or brief, found upon search in the treasury of Spain and sent to the Commissioners in England, was supplied. And so should judgment have been given by the Pope accordingly, had not the King, upon intelligence thereof, before the same judgment, appealed to the next general Council. After whose appeal the Cardinal sat upon the matter no longer.

It happened that before the matter of the said matrimony was brought in question, when I, in talk with Sir Thomas More, with a certain joy commended unto him the happy estate of this realm, that had so Catholic a Prince that no heretic durst show his face, so virtuous and learned a clergy, so grave and sound a nobility, so loving and obedient subjects, all in one faith agreeing together.

"True it is indeed, son Roper," quoth he, and in commending all degrees and estates of the same went far beyond me, "and yet, son Roper, I pray God," said he, "that some of us, as high as we seem to sit upon the mountains, treading heretics under our feet like ants, live not to see the day that we gladly would wish to be at league and accord with them, to let them have their churches quietly to themselves, so that they would be content to let us have ours quietly to ourselves." After I had told him many considerations why he had no cause to say so, "Well, well," said he, "I pray God, son Roper, some of us live not till that day," showing me no reason why I should feel any doubt thereof. To whom I said, "By my troth, sir, it is very desperately spoken," the vile term (I cry God mercy) did I use to him, who by these words perceiving me in a fume, said merrily unto me, "Well, son Roper, it shall not be so, it shall not be so." Whom in sixteen years and more, being in his house conversant with him, I could never perceive so much as once to fume.

But now to return again where I left off. After supplying the imperfections of the dispensation sent, as before rehearsed, to the Commissioners in England, the King, taking the matter for

233

ended and then meaning to proceed no further in that matter, assigned the Bishop of Durham and Sir Thomas More to go as ambassadors to Cambrai, a place neither imperial nor French, to make a treaty of peace between the French King, the Emperor, and himself. In concluding whereof, Sir Thomas More so worthily handled himself, procuring in our league far more benefits to his realm than at that time the King and Council could possibly have achieved, that for his good service on that voyage, the King, when he afterward made him Lord Chancellor, caused the Duke of Norfolk openly to declare to the people, as you shall hear hereafter more at large, how much all England was indebted to him.

Now, upon the coming home of the Bishop of Durham and Sir Thomas More from Cambrai, the King was as earnest in persuading Sir Thomas More to agree to the matter of his marriage as before, by many and divers ways urging him thereto. For which cause, as it was thought, the King rather soon after made him Lord Chancellor, and further declared unto him that though at his going over the sea to Cambrai he was in utter despair of it, yet he had conceived since some good hope to accomplish it. For albeit his first marriage, though against the positive law of the Church, and the written law of God, was supported by the dispensation, yet there was another thing found out of late, he said, whereby this marriage appeared to be so directly against the laws of nature that it could in no wise by the Church be dispensable, as Dr. Stokesley, whom he had then newly preferred to be Bishop of London, and chiefly trusted in the case, was able to instruct him, with whom he beseeched Sir

Thomas More on that point to confer. But for all his conference with him, Sir Thomas More saw nothing of such force as could induce him to change his opinion therein; which notwithstanding, the bishop showed himself, in his report of him to the King's Highness, so good and favorable, that he said he found him in his Grace's cause very ready and desirous to find some good matter wherewith he might truly serve his Grace to his contentment.

This Bishop Stokesley, being not long before in the Star Chamber openly put to rebuke by the Cardinal and committed to the Fleet,[21] not brooking this contumelious usage, thought that forasmuch as the Cardinal, for lack of such forwardness in expediting the King's divorce as his Grace looked for, was out of his Highness' favor, he had now a good occasion offered him to avenge his quarrel against him. So further to incense the King's displeasure towards him, he busily labored to invent some plausible device for the King's furtherance in that matter. Which, as before is mentioned, he revealed to his Grace, hoping thereby to bring the King to the better liking of himself, and the more disliking of the Cardinal.

His Highness [Wolsey] therefore was soon after displaced from his office, and the same in his stead was committed to Sir Thomas More (the rather to move him to incline to the King's side). Who between the Dukes of Norfolk and Suffolk was brought through Westminster Hall to his place in the Chancery, and the Duke of Norfolk, in audience of all the people there

[21] The famous London prison that took its name from its location near the Fleet stream that flowed into the Thames.

assembled, showed that he was straightly charged by special commission from the King himself, there openly, in the presence of all, to make declaration how much all England was beholden to Sir Thomas More for his good service, and how worthy he was to have the highest office in the realm, and how dearly his Grace loved and trusted him; for which, said the Duke, he had great cause to rejoice. Whereto Sir Thomas More, among his many other humble and wise sayings (not now in my memory) answered that although he had good cause to rejoice in his Highness' singular favor towards him, that he had far above his deserts so highly commended him; yet nevertheless he must for his own part needs confess that in all things alleged by his Grace he had done no more than was his duty. And further disparaged himself as unmeet for that office wherein, considering how wise and honorable a prelate had lately before taken so great a fall, he had, he said, "no cause to rejoice thereof." And as they on the King's behalf charged him uprightly to minister impartial justice to the people without corruption or affection, so did he likewise charge them again, that if they saw him at any time in anything digress from any part of his duty, in that honorable office, then, as they would discharge their own duty and fidelity to God and the King, so should they not fail to disclose it to his Grace, who otherwise might have just occasion to lay his fault wholly to their charge.

While he was Lord Chancellor, being at leisure—as seldom he was—one of his sons-in-law once said merrily to him that when Cardinal Wolsey was Lord Chancellor, not only divers members of his Privy Chamber but such also as were his door-keepers got great gain; and since he had married one of Sir Thomas More's daughters, and still kept attendance upon him, he thought he might of reason look for some reward. Yet he indeed, although he was ready himself to hear every man, poor and rich, and keep no doors shut from them, could find none open for himself, which was a great discouragement. And whereas some for friendship, some for kindred, and some for profit, would gladly have his furtherance in bringing them to Sir Thomas More's presence, if he should now take any reward from them he knew, he said, he should do them great wrong, because they might do as much for themselves as he could do for them; which condition, although he thought very commendable in Sir Thomas More, yet to him he said, being his son, he found it not profitable.

When he had told his father-in-law this tale, "You say well, son," quoth he, "I do not dislike it that you are of conscience so scrupulous, but there are many other ways, son, that I may do both yourself good, and please your friend also. For sometimes I may in words stand your friend in good stead, and sometimes I may by my letters help you and him, or if he have a case pending before me, at your request I may hear him before another, or if his case be not of the best, yet I may move the parties to fall to some reasonable end by arbitrament. Howbeit, this one thing I assure you on my faith, that if the parties will at my hand call for justice, then were it my father stood on one side and the devil on the other side (if his cause were good), the devil should have right." So he offered his son, as he thought, he said, as much favor as with reason he could require. And that he would in no respect digress from justice well appeared by a plain example of another of his sons-in-law, Mr. Heron. For when he, having a matter before his father-in-law in the Chancery, presumed too much on his favor, and would in no wise be persuaded by him to agree to an impartial order, then made his father-in-law in conclusion a flat decree against him.

This Lord Chancellor used commonly every afternoon to sit in his open hall, to the intent that if any person had any suit to bring to him, he might the more boldly come into his presence, and there open complaint before him. Whose manner was also to read every bill himself, ere he would award any subpoena, which if it bore matter sufficiently worthy a subpoena, he would set his hand to, or else cancel it. Whenever he passed through Westminster Hall to his place in the Chancery by the Court of the King's Bench, if his father, one of the judges there, had been seated ere he came, he would go into the same court, and there reverently kneeling down in the sight of them all duly ask his father's blessing. And if it happened that his father and he at readings in Lincoln's Inn met together, as they sometimes did, notwithstanding his high office, he would offer the pre-eminence in argument to his father, though the latter for his office' sake would refuse to take it. And for the better declaration of his natural affection towards his father, he not only (when the old man lay on his deathbed) came to visit him, as was his duty, ofttimes with comfortable and most kindly words; but also at his departure out of this world, taking him about the neck, with tears most lovingly kissed and embraced him, commending him into the merciful hands of Almighty God, and so departed from him.

And as few injunctions as he granted while he was Lord Chancellor, yet were they by some of the judges of the law disliked, which I understanding declared the same to Sir Thomas More, who answered me that they had little cause to find fault with him therefore. And thereupon he caused one Mr. Crooke, chief of the six clerks, to make a docket containing the whole number and causes of all such injunctions, as either in his time had already been issued, or at that present time were pending before him in any of the King's Courts at Westminster. Which done, he invited all the judges to dinner with him in the Council Chamber at Westminster, where after dinner he broke to them what complaints he had heard of his injunctions, and moreover showed them both the number and causes of every one of them in order so plainly that, upon full debating of those matters, they were all forced to confess that they, in like case, could have done no otherwise themselves. And then offered he this to them, that if the justices of every court, to whom the reformation of the rigor of the law, by reason of their office, most specially pertained, would, upon reasonable considerations, by their own discretion (as they were, as he thought, in conscience bound) mitigate and reform the rigor of the law themselves, there would from thenceforth by him be no more injunctions granted. Whereupon, when they refused to condescend, said he to them: "Forasmuch as yourselves, my lords, drive me to that necessity for awarding our injunctions to relieve the people's injury, you cannot hereafter any more justly blame me." After that he said secretly to me: "I perceive, son, why they like not to do so. For they see that they may, through the verdict of the jury, cast all reproach away from themselves upon them whom they count their chief defense, and therefore I am compelled to endure the peril of all such reports."

And as little leisure as he had to spend in the study of Holy Scripture and controversies upon religion and such other like virtuous exercises, being in manner continually busied about the affairs of the King and the realm, yet he assuredly took care and pains in setting forth divers profitable works in defense of the true Catholic religion against heresies, secretly sown abroad in the realm, that the bishops, to whose pastoral care the reformation thereof principally appertained, thinking themselves by his toil (wherein by their own confession, they were not able to compare with him) discharged of their duty, and considering that, for all his pains and Prince's favor, he was no rich man nor in yearly revenues as advanced as his worthiness deserved, therefore at a convocation among themselves and others of the clergy, agreed together, and concluded upon a sum of four or five thousand pounds at the least (to my remembrance) to recompense him for his pains. To the payment whereof every bishop, abbot, and the rest of the clergy were, after the rate of their abilities, liberal contributors, hoping this portion should be to his contentment.

Whereupon Tunstall, Bishop of Durham, Clarke, Bishop of Bath, and (as far as I can call to mind) Vaysie, Bishop of Exeter, repaired unto him, declaring to him how thankfully for his efforts bestowed upon their charge in God's cause they reckoned themselves bound to consider him. And that albeit they could not according to his deserts so worthily as they gladly would requite him therefor, but reserved that only to the goodness of God, yet for a small part of recompense, in respect of his estate so unequal to his worthiness, in the name of their whole Convocation, they presented unto him that sum which they desired him to take in good part,—who, declining it, said that like as it was no small comfort to him, that so wise and learned men so well accepted his simple doing, for which he intended never to receive reward but at the hands of God only, to whom alone was thanks thereof chiefly to be ascribed; so gave he most humble thanks unto their honors all for their bountiful consideration.

When they, for all their importunate pressing on him, until few would have believed he could have refused it, could by no means make him take it, they then besought him to consent that they might bestow it upon his wife and children. "Not so, my Lords," quoth he, "I had rather see it all cast into the Thames than that I or any of mine should have thereof the worth of one penny. For though your offer, my Lords, is indeed very friendly and honorable, yet set I so much by my pleasure, and so little by my profit, that I would not, in good faith, for that much and much more have lost the rest of many a night's sleep as was spent upon those books. And yet, for all that, I would wish, on condition that all heresies were suppressed, that all my books were burned and my labor utterly lost." Thus departing, they were fain to restore to every man his own again.

This Lord Chancellor, albeit he was to God and the world well known for notable virtue, though not so by every man considered, yet for the avoidance of singularity he would not appear otherwise than other men in his apparel and outward behavior. And albeit he appeared honorable outwardly, and like one of his calling, yet inwardly, no such vanities esteeming, he secretly wore next his body a shirt of hair, which my sister More, a young gentlewoman, chancing to espy as he sat in the summer at supper alone in his doublet and hose, wearing thereon a plain shirt without ruff or collar, began to laugh at it. My wife, not ignorant of his habit, perceiving the same privately told him of it, and he being sorry that she saw it, presently amended it. He used also sometimes to punish his body with whips, the cords knotted, which was known only to my wife, his eldest daughter; whom for her secrecy above all others he specially trusted, causing her, as need required, to wash the same shirt of hair.

Now shortly upon his entry into the high office of the Chancellorship, the King soon again bade him weigh and consider his greatest concern, but he, falling down upon his knees, humbly besought his Highness to remain his gracious Sovereign, as ever since his entry into his gracious service he had found him, saying there was nothing in the world that had been so grievous to his heart as to remember that he was not able, as he willingly would have been, with the loss of one of his limbs, for that matter, to find anything whereby he could serve his

Grace's contentment; as he always bare in mind the most godly words, that his Highness spoke to him at his first coming into his noble service, the most virtuous lesson that ever prince taught his servant, desiring him first to look to God, and after God to him, as in good faith, he said, he did, or else might his Grace well account him his most unworthy servant. To this the King answered that if he could not with his conscience serve him, he was content to accept his service otherwise, and use the advice of others of his learned Council, whose consciences could well enough agree thereto. He would nevertheless continue his gracious favor towards him, and never with that matter molest his conscience after.

But Sir Thomas More, in process of time, saw the King fully determined to proceed with the marriage of Queen Anne, and he with the bishops and nobles of the Higher House of Parliament were, for the furtherance of that marriage, commanded by the King to go down to the House of Commons to show to them both what the Universities of other parts beyond the seas as well as at Oxford and Cambridge had done in that behalf, their seals also testifying the same. All these matters he, at the King's request (not showing of what mind himself was therein), made known to the Lower House of the Parliament. Nevertheless, doubting lest further attempts should follow after, into which, contrary to his conscience, by reason of his office he was likely to be brought, he made suit to the Duke of Norfolk, his singular dear friend, to be a mediator to the King, that he might, with his Grace's favor, be discharged from that onerous office of the Chancellorship, wherein for certain infirmities of his body, he pretended himself unable any longer to serve.

This Duke, coming on a time to Chelsea to dine with him, chanced to find him at church singing in the choir with a surplice on his back; to whom after service, as they went home together arm in arm, the Duke said, "God body, God body, my lord Chancellor, a parish clerk, a parish clerk, you dishonor the King and his office." "Nay," quoth Sir Thomas More, smiling upon the Duke, "your Grace must not think that the King, your master and mine, will be offended with me for serving God his Master, or thereby count his office dishonored."

When the Duke, being solicited thereto by importunate suit, had at length obtained for Sir Thomas More a clear discharge from his office, then at a time convenient, by his Highness' appointment he repaired to his Grace, to yield up to him the great seal; which his Grace, with thanks and praise for his worthy service in that office, courteously received at his hands. And it pleased his Highness to say further to him that for the good service he had done him, in any suit which he should hereafter bring to him, that either should concern his honor (for that word it pleased his Highness to use to him) or that should pertain to his profit, he would find his Highness a good and gracious lord to him.

After he had thus given over his Chancellorship, and placed all his gentlemen and yeomen with bishops and noblemen, and his eight watermen with Lord Audley, who succeeded him in the same office, to whom he also gave his great barge, he then called us that were his children to him, and asked our advice, how we might now, in this decay of his ability, so impaired by the surrender of his office that he could not, as he was wont, bear the whole costs of us all himself, from henceforth be able to live and continue together, as he wished we should. When he saw us all silent, and in that case not ready to show our opinions to him, "Then will I," said he, "show my poor mind to you. I have been brought up at Oxford, at an Inn of Chancery, at Lincoln's Inn, and in the King's Court, so up from the lowest degree to the highest, and yet have I, in yearly revenues little more than one hundred pounds by the year at this present left me. So that we must needs hereafter, if we like to live together, be contented to become contributors together. But by my counsel it shall not be best for us to fall to the lowest fare first. We will not therefore descend to Oxford fare, nor to the fare of New Inn, but we will begin with Lincoln's Inn diet, on which many right worshipful and of good years do live full well. Which if we find ourselves the first year not able to maintain, then will we the next year after go one step down to New Inn fare, wherewith many an honest man is well contented. If that exceed our ability too, then will we the next year after descend to Oxford fare, whereon many grave, ancient, and learned Fathers live continually. And if our ability stretch not to maintain that neither, then may we yet with bags and wallets go a-begging together and, hoping that for pity some good folks will give their charity, at every man's door sing *salve Regina*,[22] and so still keep company merrily together."

[22] One of the antiphons of the Virgin, which begins *"Salve Regina, mater misericordiae."* (Hail, O Queen, mother of pity.)

And whereas you have heard before how he was taken by the King from a very worshipful living into his Grace's service, and how in all the great and weighty cases of the realm that concerned his Highness, he consumed and spent painful care, travail, and trouble beyond the seas as well as within the realm, in effect the whole substance of his life; yet with all the gain he got thereby (being never a wasteful spender thereof) he was not able, after the resignation of his office as Lord Chancellor, to find sufficient meat, drink, fuel, apparel, and such other necessary charges for the maintenance of himself, and those who necessarily belonged to him. All the land that ever he purchased before he was Lord Chancellor was not, I am well assured, above the value of twenty marks [23] by the year, and after his debts were paid he had not, I know, his chain excepted, left him in gold and silver the worth of one hundred pounds. And whereas, upon holidays, during his high chancellorship, one of his gentlemen, when service at the church was over, used ordinarily to come to my Lady his wife's pew and say, "Madam, my Lord is gone," the next holiday after the surrender of his office and departure of his gentlemen, he came unto my Lady his wife's pew himself, and making a low curtsey said to her, "Madam, my Lord is gone."

In the time somewhat before his trouble, he would talk with his wife and children of the joys of heaven and the pains of hell, of the lives of holy martyrs, and of their grievous martyrdom, of their marvelous patience, and of their passions and

[23] A mark was worth 13s.4d. It was in common usage in England until the eighteenth century.

deaths, how they suffered rather than offend God, and what a happy and a blessed thing it was for the love of God to suffer loss of goods, imprisonment, loss of lands, and life also. He would further say to them that upon his faith, if he might perceive his wife and children would encourage him to die in a good cause, it would so comfort him, that for very joy thereof, it would make him run merrily to his death. He showed them beforehand what trouble might befall him later, and with like virtuous talk he so long before his trouble encouraged them that when he afterward fell in trouble indeed, his trouble to him was a great deal the less, *quia spicula praevisa minus laedunt*.[24] Now upon his resignation of his office came Sir Thomas Cromwell, then in the King's high favor, to Chelsea to him with a message from the King, whereon when they had thoroughly communed together, "Mr. Cromwell," quoth he, "you are now entered into the service of a most noble, wise, and liberal prince; if you will follow my poor advice you will, in giving counsel to his Grace, ever tell him what he ought to do, but never tell him what he is able to do; so shall you show yourself a true faithful servant, and a right worthy Councilor. For if the lion knew his own strength, hard were it for any man to rule him."

Shortly thereupon was there a commission directed to Cranmer, then Archbishop of Canterbury, to determine the matter of the matrimony between the King and Queen Katherine at St. Alban's.[25] So he, pretending that he had no

24 "Pricks foreseen cause less pain."
25 The court which judged the marriage void sat at Dunstable, not at St.

justice at the Pope's hands, from thenceforth separated himself from the See of Rome, and so married the Lady Anne Bullen; which Sir Thomas More, understanding, said to me, "God give grace, son, that these acts within a while be not confirmed with oaths." I, at that time, seeing no likelihood thereof, yet fearing lest for his forespeaking it would the sooner come to pass, waxed therefore for his saying much offended with him.

It chanced not long before the coming of Queen Anne through the streets of London from the Tower to Westminster to her Coronation that Sir Thomas More received a letter from the Bishops of Durham, Bath, and Winchester, requesting him to bear them company from the Tower to the Coronation and also to take twenty pounds, that by the bearer thereof they had sent him, to buy a gown with; which he thankfully received, and remained at home, and at their next meeting said merrily to them, "My Lords, in the letter which you lately sent me, you required two things of me; since I was so well contented to grant you one, I thought I might therefore be the bolder to deny you the other."

In continuation, when the King saw that he could by no manner of benefits win Sir Thomas More to his side, then went he about by terrors and threats to drive him thereunto. The beginning of which trouble grew by occasion of a certain

---

Alban's, as Roper has it; and Henry and Anne were married before the judgment was given, not afterward. It had been a secret marriage, however, and was not declared lawful, or announced openly until after the Dunstable decision was given.

nun [26] dwelling in Canterbury, for her virtue and holiness
no little esteemed among the people, unto whom for that
cause many religious persons, Doctors of Divinity, and divers
others of good worship of the laity used to resort. She affirmed
that she had revelations from God to give the King warning
of his wicked life, and of the abuses of the sword and authority
committed to him by God; and understanding that my Lord
of Rochester, Bishop Fisher, was a man noted for his virtuous
living and learning, she repaired to Rochester and there disclosed to him all her revelations, desiring his advice and counsel therein. The Bishop, perceiving that this might well stand
with the laws of God and his Church, advised her (as she
before had warning and intended) to go to the King herself,
and to let him understand the whole circumstance thereof.
Whereupon she went unto the King, and told him all her
revelations, and returned home again. And in short space after,
she, making a journey to the Nun of Sion, by means of one
Mr. Reynolds, a father of that house there chanced to enter
into talk with Sir Thomas More concerning such secrets as
she had revealed unto her, some part whereof seemed to touch
on the matter of the King's supremacy and marriage (which
shortly thereupon followed). He, notwithstanding he might

26 This was Elizabeth Barton, who acquired fame as the Holy Maid of Kent
through her pretended revelations of divine origin. For about eight years
(1526-1534) she was sought by people of all classes for counsel and advice.
Members of the clergy who championed Queen Katherine's cause led her to
utter prophecies and warnings to King Henry respecting his proposed divorce.
The hoax was uncovered by Cranmer, and after confessing that she was an
imposter, Elizabeth, with several of her confederates, was executed in 1534.

well at that time without danger of any law freely and safely have talked with her thereon (though afterwards, as he himself had prognosticated, those matters were established by statutes and confirmed by oaths), nevertheless, in all the conversation between them, as in process of time it appeared, always so discreetly conducted himself that he deserved not to be blamed, but contrariwise to be commended and praised.

And had he not been one that in all his great office, and doings for the King and realm together kept himself so clear from all corruption of wrongdoing or bribes-taking that no man was able therewith to blemish him, it would without doubt (in this troublesome time of the King's wrath and indignation towards him) have been deeply laid to his charge, and accepted as favoring the King's Highness, as in the case of one Parnell it most manifestly appeared; against whom Sir Thomas More, while he was Lord Chancellor, at the suit of one Vaughn, his adversary, had made a decree. This Parnell grievously complained to the King's Highness that Sir Thomas More, for making the decree, had from the same Vaughn (unable for gout to travel abroad himself) by the hands of his wife taken a great gilt cup for a bribe. Sir Thomas More thereupon by the King's appointment was called before the Council, where that matter was heinously laid up to his charge, and forthwith confessed, that forasmuch as that cup was long after the aforesaid decree brought to him for a New Year's gift, he upon her importunate pressing it upon him, therefore out of courtesy had not refused to take it. Then the Lord of Wiltshire [27] (for hatred of his religion preferrer of this suit) with rejoicing said to the Lords, "Lo my Lords, lo, did I not tell you that you should find this matter true?" Whereupon Sir Thomas More desired their worships, that as they courteously heard him tell one part of his tale, so they would vouchsafe of their honors impartially to hear the other. After which promise obtained, he further declared to them that albeit indeed he had after much entreaty received that cup, yet immediately thereupon he caused his butler to fill it with wine, and of that cup drank to her; and that when she had pledged him, then as freely as her husband had given it to him, even so freely gave he the same to her again, to give to her husband for his New Year's gift, which at his urgent request, though much against her will, she was at length willing to receive, as she herself and certain others there presently deposed before them. Thus was the great mountain cut down to a molehill.

So I remember that another time on a New Year's day there came to him one Mrs. Crocker, a rich widow (for whom with no small pains he had made a decree in the Chancery against the Lord of Arundel), to present him with a pair of gloves and forty pounds in angels [28] in them for a New Year's gift. From

[27] The Lord of Wiltshire was Thomas Boleyn, father of Anne. He was attached to the court of Henry VIII, and carried on various diplomatic missions for the King and Wolsey. During the time when Anne was in favor with the King, many honors and distinctions were accorded him.

[28] A gold coin first minted in 1465 as a new issue of the *noble,* a standard coin of the period. Because it bore the imprint of the archangel Michael standing on the dragon, the coin soon became known as the *angel.* When first struck, the angel was worth 6s.8d, but in the reign of Edward VI it was valued at 10s. The angel was last coined in the reign of Charles I.

her he thankfully received the gloves, but refusing the money said to her, "Mistress, since it were against good manners to reject a gentlewoman's New Year's gift, I am content to receive your gloves, but as for your money, I utterly refuse." So, much against her mind, he forced her to take her gold again. And one Mr. Gresham likewise, having a case pending in the Chancery against him, sent Sir Thomas More for a New Year's gift a fair gilt cup, the fashion whereof he very well liking, caused one of his own, though not to his fancy of so good a fashion, yet richer in value, to be brought out of his chamber, which he told the messenger to deliver to his mistress in recompense, and under no other conditions would he receive it. Many things more of like effect for declaration of his innocence and his clearness from corruption or evil affection, could I here rehearse besides, but omitting them to avoid tediousness, I refer the readers with these few fore-remembered examples, to their own judgments wisely to consider.

At this Parliament there was brought into the House of Lords a bill to accuse the nun and divers other religious persons of high treason, and the Bishop of Rochester, Sir Thomas More, and certain others of failing to disclose treason. The King supposed that this bill would be to Sir Thomas More so troublous and terrible that it would force him to relent and consent to his request, wherein his Grace was much deceived. To which bill Sir Thomas More made suit to be received personally in his own defense to make answer; but the King, not liking that, assigned the Archbishop of Canterbury, the Lord Chancellor, the Duke of Norfolk, and Mr. Cromwell, at a day and place appointed, to call Sir Thomas More before them. At which time I, thinking I had good opportunity, earnestly advised him to labor with these Lords for their help to remove his name from the Parliament bill; who answered me, he would. And at his coming before them according to their appointment, they entertained him in very friendly fashion, desiring him to sit down with them, which in no wise he would. Then began the Lord Chancellor to declare unto him in how many ways the King had showed his love and favor towards him, how heartily he would have had him continue in his office, how glad he would have been to have heaped more benefits upon him, and finally, how he could ask no worldly honor, or profit at his Highness' hands that were likely to be denied him; thus hoping by declaration of the King's kindness and favor towards him to persuade him to recompense his Grace with like kindness again, and to yield his consent to those things that the Parliament, the Bishops, and Universities had already passed.

To this Sir Thomas More mildly answered saying, "No man living is there, my Lords, that would with better will do the thing that would be acceptable to the King's Highness than I who must needs confess his manifold benefits, and bountiful goodness most benignly bestowed upon me. Howbeit I verily hoped that I should never have heard of this matter again, considering that I have from time to time always from the beginning so plainly and truly declared my mind unto his Grace, which his Highness to me ever seemed, like a most gracious prince, very well to accept, never intending, as he said, to molest me more therewith. Since which time I could never find any further thing that was able to move me to any change; and if I could, there is none in all the world that would have been gladder of it than I."

Many more things of like sort were there uttered on both sides. But in the end when they saw they could by no persuasion move him from his former determination, then began they more severely to take him to task, telling him that the King's Highness had commanded them, if they could by no gentleness win him, to charge him in his name with great ingratitude, and say that never was there a servant so villainous to his master, nor a subject so traitorous to his prince as he. For he by his subtle, sinister cunning had most unnaturally procured and incited him to publish a book of the *Assertion of Seven Sacraments*,[29] and in maintenance of the Pope's authority, had caused him, to his dishonor throughout all Christendom, to put a sword in the Pope's hands to fight against himself.

When they had thus set forth all the terrors they could imagine against him, "My Lords," quoth he, "these terrors are arguments for children, and not for me. But to answer that wherewith you do chiefly accuse me, I believe the King's Highness of his honor will never lay that to my charge. For none is there that in that point can say more in my excuse than his

[29] The *Assertion of the Sacraments* was the book in which Henry VIII attacked Luther's theories, winning thereby Pope Leo's gratitude and the title "Defender of the Faith," that was soon to appear an ironical epithet. Luther replied to Henry in a stinging pamphlet in 1522, and the next year More answered for the King with his *Vindication of Henry Against Luther*.

Highness himself, who right well knows that I was never a procurer or councilor of his Majesty thereto, but that after it was finished was by his Grace's appointment, and consent of the authors of the same, only a sorter out and arranger of the principal subjects therein contained. In which, when I found the Pope's authority highly advanced, and with strong arguments mightily defended, I said to his Grace, 'I must put your Grace in remembrance of one thing, and that is this. The Pope, as your Grace knows, is a prince as you are, and in league with all other Christian princes; and it may hereafter so fall out that your Grace and he may vary upon some points of the league, whereupon may grow some breach of amity and war between you both; I think it best therefore that that part be amended, and his authority more lightly touched.'

" 'Nay,' quoth his Grace, 'it shall not. We are so much bounden unto the See of Rome that we cannot do too much honor to it.' Then did I further put him in remembrance of the Statute of Praemunire,[30] whereby a good part of the Pope's pastoral authority here was taken away. To that answered his Highness, 'Whatsoever impediment there be to the contrary, we will proclaim that authority to the uttermost. For we received from that See our Crown Imperial'; which till his Grace with his own mouth told me I never heard of before. So I trust

[30] The first *Statute of Praemunire* in 1353 declared against those who were taking cases out of the kingdom "of which the cognizance pertains to our lord the King." A second statute of 1393 definitely mentioned the Court of Rome and railed against those who "in derogation of our lord the King's regality, bring suit in the court of another." It is obvious that the roots of English anti-papal sentiment lay deep in the past.

when his Grace shall be truly informed of this, and shall call to his gracious remembrance my doings on that behalf, his Highness will never speak more of it, but will clear me thoroughly therein himself." And thus unpleasantly they departed.

Then Sir Thomas More took his boat towards his house at Chelsea, wherein along the way he was very merry; and for that I was not sorry, hoping he had got himself released from the Parliament bill. When he was come home, then we two walked alone in his garden together, where I, desirous to know how he had sped, said, "Sir, I trust all is well, because you are so merry." "That is so, indeed, son Roper, I thank God," quoth he. "Are you taken out of the Parliament bill then?" I said. "By my troth, son Roper," quoth he, "I never remembered it." "Never remembered it, sir?" quoth I. "A case that touches yourself so nearly, and us all for your sake. I am sorry to hear it. For I verily trusted when I saw you so merry that all had been well." Then said he, "Wilt thou know, son Roper, why I was so merry?" "That I would gladly, sir," quoth I. "In good faith I rejoiced, son," quoth he, "that I had given the devil so foul a fall, and that with those Lords I had gone so far that without great shame I could never go back again." At which words I waxed very sad. For though himself liked it well, yet I liked it but little.

Now upon the report made by the Lord Chancellor and the other Lords to the King of all their discourse with Sir Thomas More, the King was so highly offended with him that he plainly told them he was fully determined that the said Parlia-

ment bill should undoubtedly proceed forward against him.
To whom my Lord Chancellor and the rest of the Lords said
that they perceived the Lords of the Upper House to be so
resolutely bent to hear him make answer for himself in his
own case that if he were not removed from the Parliament
bill, there would without fail be an utter overthrow of it all.
But for all this the King must needs have his own will therein,
or else he said that at the passing thereof he would be personally present himself. Then the Lord Audley and the rest,
seeing him so vehemently set thereon, most humbly on their
knees besought his Majesty to refrain from the same, considering that if he should in his own presence receive a refusal, it
would not only encourage his subjects ever after to resist him,
but it would throughout all Christendom redound to his dishonor forever. They added thereto that they mistrusted not in
time to find some fit means to serve his Grace's turn better. For
in this case of the nun, Sir Thomas More was accounted so innocent and clear that for his dealing therein men reckoned him
worthier of praise than reproof. Whereupon at length, through
their earnest persuasion, he was content to condescend to their
petition. And on the morrow after, Mr. Cromwell meeting me
in Parliament House wished me to tell my father that he was
taken out of the Parliament bill. But because I had appointed
to dine that day in London, I sent the message by my servant
to my wife at Chelsea, whereof she informed her father. "In
faith, Meg," quoth he, *"quod defertur, non aufertur."* [31]

[31] "What is put off is not ended."

After this, as the Duke of Norfolk and Sir Thomas More chanced to fall in familiar talk together, the Duke said unto him, "By the Mass, Mr. More, it is perilous striving with princes, and therefore I would wish you to incline somewhat to the King's pleasure. For by God's body, Mr. More, *indignatio principis mors est*." [32] "Is that all, my Lord?" quoth he. "Is there, in good faith, no more difference between your grace and me but that I shall die today and you tomorrow?"

So it fell out within a month or thereabout after the passing of the Statute for the oath of Supremacy and Matrimony,[33] that all the priests of London and Westminster, and he the one layman were sent to appear at Lambeth before the Bishop of Canterbury, the Lord Chancellor, and Secretary Cromwell, Commissioners there, to tender the oath to them. Then Sir Thomas More, as was always his accustomed manner ere he entered into any matter of importance (as when he was first chosen for the King's Privy Council, when he was sent Ambassador, appointed Speaker of the Parliament, made Lord Chancellor, or when he took any like weighty matter upon him) to go to the church, and be confessed, hear mass, and receive the sacrament; so did he likewise in the morning early the self-same day that he was summoned to appear before the Lords at Lambeth. And whereas he used always before, at his de-

[32] "The anger of the Prince is death."

[33] This was the Act of March 1534, that fixed the succession on the children of Henry and Anne Boleyn. More did not deny the right of the King and Parliament to legislate on this matter, but refused the oath in the form in which it was presented to him. In November of the same year, another statute was passed to legalize the oath in the form which he had refused.

parture from his house and children, whom he loved tenderly, to have them bring him to his boat, and there to kiss them all, and bid them farewell, on this occasion he would suffer none of them to follow him beyond the gate, but pulled the wicket after him, and shut them all away from him, and with a heavy heart, as by his countenance it appeared, there took the boat with me and our four servants towards Lambeth. Wherein sitting still sadly awhile, at last he whispered in my ear and said, "Son Roper, I thank our Lord, the field is won." What he meant thereby, then, I knew not. Yet loth to seem ignorant, I answered, "Sir, I am very glad thereof." But as I conjectured afterwards it was because the love he had for God wrought in him so effectually that it utterly conquered in him all his carnal affection.

At his coming to Lambeth, how wisely he behaved himself before the Commissioners at the ministration of the oath unto him, may be found in certain letters of his sent to my wife, remaining in a great book of his works. There within four days he was taken into the custody of the Abbot of Westminster, during which time the King consulted with his Council what order was meet to be taken with him. And albeit in the beginning they were resolved he would be discharged with an oath whereby he would not let it be known whether he had taken the oath of Supremacy or what he thought thereof. Yet did Queen Anne, by her importunate clamor, so annoy and exasperate the King against him that, contrary to his former resolution, he caused the oath of Supremacy to be ministered unto him. Then he, albeit he made a discreet and qualified answer, nevertheless was forthwith committed to the Tower, and as he was going thitherward, wearing, as he commonly did, a chain of gold about his neck, Sir Richard Cromwell (that had the charge of his conveyance thither) advised him to send home his chain to his wife, or some of his children. "Nay, sir," quoth he, "that I will not. For if I were taken in the field by my enemies, I would want them to fare somewhat better by me."

At whose arrival at the Tower gate Mr. Lieutenant was ready to receive him, and the porter demanded of him his upper garment. "Mr. Porter," quoth he, "here it is," and took off his cap and delivered it to him, saying, "I am very sorry it is not better for you." "Nay, sir," quoth the porter, "I must have your gown." And then was he by Mr. Lieutenant conveyed to his lodging, where he called to him one John a-Wood, his own servant, appointed to attend him there, who could neither write nor read, and swore him before the Lieutenant that if he should hear, or see him at any time, speak or write any manner of thing against the King, the Council, or the state of the realm, he should speak of it to the Lieutenant, that the Lieutenant might straightway reveal it to the Council.

Now when Sir Thomas More had remained in the Tower a little more than a month, my wife, longing to see her father, by her earnest entreaty at length got leave to go to him. At whose coming, after the seven psalms and litany were said, which whenever she came to him, ere he fell in talk of any worldly matters he was accustomed to say with her, among other conversation he said to her:

"I believe, Meg, that they that have put me here think they have done me a high displeasure. But I assure you on my faith, mine own dear daughter, if it had not been for my wife and you that are my children, whom I count the chief part of my charge, I would not have failed, long ere this, to have closed myself in as narrow a room and narrower too.[34] But since I come hither not of my own desert, I trust that God of his goodness will discharge me of my responsibility, and with his gracious help make up for my absence among you. I find no cause, I thank God, Meg, to reckon myself in worse case here than in my own house; for methinks God makes of me a pampered pet, and sets me on his lap and dandles me."

Thus by his gracious demeanor in tribulations it appeared that all the troubles that ever chanced to befall him, by his patient sufferance thereof, were to him no painful punishment but through his patience became profitable exercises. And at another time, when he had first questioned my wife a while concerning the condition of his wife and children, and the state of his house in his absence, he asked her how Queen Anne did. "In faith, father, never better," quoth she. "Never better, Meg?" quoth he. "Alas, Meg, alas, it saddens me to think into what misery she, poor soul, shortly shall come."

After this, Mr. Lieutenant, coming into his chamber to visit him, rehearsed the benefits and friendships that he had many times received at his hands, and how much bounden he was therefore to entertain him in friendly fashion and make him good cheer. But since, the case standing as it did, he could not do this without incurring the King's indignation, he trusted,

[34] More here refers to a monk's cell. The monastic life had always held a great appeal for him.

he said, that he would accept his good will, and such poor cheer as he had. "Mr. Lieutenant," quoth he again, "I verily believe, as you may be, so are you my good friend indeed, and would, as you say, with your best cheer entertain me; for which I most heartily thank you. And assure yourself, Mr. Lieutenant," quoth he, "I do not dislike my cheer, but whenever I do so, then thrust me out of your doors."

The oath confirming the supremacy and matrimony was by the first statute comprised in few words, but the Lord Chancellor and Mr. Secretary did of their own accord add more words to it, to make it appear to the King's ears more pleasant and plausible. And that oath, so amplified, they caused to be ministered to Sir Thomas More and to all others throughout the realm; which Sir Thomas More, perceiving, said to my wife:

"I may tell thee, Meg, they that have committed me hither for refusing the oath, which does not conform to the statute, are not by their own law to justify my imprisonment. And, surely, daughter, it is a great pity that a Christian prince should, by a flexible council ready to follow his wishes, and a weak clergy, lacking grace constantly to stand by their learning, be abused with such shameful flattery." But at length the Lord Chancellor and Mr. Secretary, espying their oversight in that behalf, were constrained afterwards to find means whereby another statute [35] should be made for the confirmation of the oath, so amplified with their additions.

[35] See p. 255, footnote 30.

After Sir Thomas More had given up his office and all other worldly doings therewith, to the intent that he might from thenceforth set himself the more quietly to the service of God, he then made a conveyance for the disposition of his lands, reserving for himself an estate thereof only for the term of his life, and after his decease assuring some part of the same to his wife, and some to his son's wife for a jointure; in consideration of the fact that she was an heiress in possession of more than a hundred pounds land by the year—and some to me and my wife in recompense for our marriage money with divers remainders besides, all which conveyance and assurance were perfectly finished long before the matter whereof he was accused was made an offense. Yet afterward it was by statute clearly declared; and so all his lands that he had by the said conveyance in such sort assured to his wife and children, contrary to the order of the law, were taken away from them, and brought into the King's hands, except for that portion that he had appointed to my wife and me, which, although he had in the aforesaid conveyance reserved, as he did the rest, for the term of his life unto himself, nevertheless, upon further consideration he afterward by another conveyance had given the same immediately to me and my wife in possession. And so because the statute had made void only the first conveyance, giving no more to the King but what was covered by it, the second conveyance which was given to my wife and me, being dated two days later, was outside the compass of the statute, and so by that means was our portion clearly reserved to us.

Sir Thomas More in the Tower chanced once upon looking out of his window to behold one Mr. Reynolds, a religious, learned, and virtuous father of Sion, and three monks of the Charterhouse going out of the Tower to execution for the matter of the supremacy. And he, as one longing to have accompanied them on that journey, said to my wife, then standing there beside him, "Lo, dost thou not see, Meg, that these blessed fathers are now as cheerful going to their deaths as bridegrooms to their marriages? Wherefore thereby thou mayest see, my own good daughter, what a difference there is between those who have in effect spent all their days in a narrow, hard, penitential, and painstaking life religiously, and those who have in the world, like worldly wretches, as thy poor father has done, licentiously consumed all their time in pleasure and ease. For God, considering their long-continued life in most sore and grievous penance, will not longer suffer them to remain here in this vale of misery and iniquity, but speedily takes them hence to the fruition of his everlasting deity. Whereas thy frail father, Meg, that, like a most wicked captive, has passed the whole course of his miserable life most pitifully, God, thinking him not worthy so soon to come to that eternal felicity, leaves him here yet, to be plunged still further in the world and harassed with misery."

A while after, Mr. Secretary, coming to him in the Tower from the King, pretended much friendship towards him, and for his comfort told him that the King's Highness was his good and gracious lord and did not bear in mind anything wherein he should have any cause of scruple, to trouble his conscience henceforth. As soon as Mr. Secretary was gone, to express what comfort he took from his words, he wrote with a coal—for ink then he had none—these verses following:

Ay flattering fortune look you never so fair,
Nor never so pleasantly begin to smile,
As though thou wouldst my ruins all repair
During my life thou shalt not me beguile.
Trust I shall, God, to enter in a while
Thy haven of heaven sure and uniform,
Ever after thy calm look I for no storm.

When Sir Thomas More had continued a good while in the Tower, my Lady his wife obtained license to see him, who at her first coming, like a simple woman and somewhat worldly, too, with this manner of salutation bluntly saluted him: "What the good year, Mr. More," [36] quoth she, "I marvel that you, that have always hitherto taken for so wise a man, will now so play the fool as to lie here in this close and filthy prison and be content to be shut up among mice and rats, when you might be abroad at your liberty, and with the favor and good will both of the King and his Council, if you would but do as all the bishops and best learned men of this realm have done. And seeing you have at Chelsea a right fair house, your library, your books, your gallery, your garden, your or-

[36] This ejaculation, as well as the expression of contempt, "Tille valle, tille valle," in the following paragraph, are common expressions of the time. One encounters them frequently in the popular literature of the Tudor period. Shakespeare uses both of them.

chards, and all other necessaries so handsomely about you, where you might, in the company of me your wife, your children, and household be merry, I wonder what in God's name you mean still thus foolishly to tarry here."

After he had a while quietly heard her, with a cheerful countenance he said to her, "I pray thee, good Mrs. Alice, tell me, tell me one thing." "What is that?" quoth she. "Is not this house as nigh heaven as mine own?" To whom she, after her accustomed fashion, not liking such talk, answered, "Tille valle, tille valle." "How say you, Mrs. Alice, is it not so?" he quoth. "*Bone Deus, bone Deus,* man, will you never stop this kind of talk?" quoth she. "Well then, Mrs. Alice, if it be so, it is very well. For I see no great cause why I should much rejoice in my gay house, or anything belonging thereunto, when if I should but seven years lie buried under ground, and then arise and come thither again, I should not fail to find some therein that would bid me get out of the door, and tell me it were none of mine. What cause have I then to like such a house as would so soon forget its master?" So her persuasion moved him but little.

Not long after this there came to him the Lord Chancellor, the Dukes of Norfolk and Suffolk, with Mr. Secretary, and certain others of the Privy Council at two separate times, by all devices possible entreating him either to confess the supremacy, or definitely to deny it.[37] Whereto, as appears by

37 The Acts of Attainder passed against Fisher and More in November 1534 carried no penalty of death, but by the Act of Treasons passed in the same month, a denial of the Royal Supremacy rendered one liable to death as a traitor.

his examination in the said great book, they could never bring
him. Shortly thereupon Mr. Rich, afterwards Lord Rich, then
newly made the King's Solicitor, Sir Richard Southwell, and
Mr. Palmer, servant to the Secretary, were sent to Sir Thomas
More in the Tower, to fetch away his books from him. And
while Sir Richard Southwell and Mr. Palmer were busy bundling up his books, Mr. Rich pretended friendly talk with him
and among other things by design, as it seemed, said this to
him: "Forasmuch as it is well known, Mr. More, that you are
a man both wise and well learned, as well in the laws of the
realm as in other things, I pray you therefore, sir, let me be so
bold as of good will to put you this case. Admit there were,
sir," quoth he, "an Act of Parliament that all the realm should
take me for the King, would not you, Mr. More, take me for
the King?" "Yes, sir," quoth Sir Thomas More, "that would
I." "I put the case further," quoth Mr. Rich, "that there were
an Act of Parliament that all the realm should take me for
the Pope; would then you not, Mr. More, take me for the
Pope?"

"For answer," quoth Sir Thomas More, "to your first case,
the Parliament may well, Mr. Rich, meddle with the state of
temporal princes; but to make answer to your second case, I
will put you this case. Suppose the Parliament should make
a law that God should not be God, would you then, Mr. Rich,
say God were not God?" "No, sir," quoth he, "that I would
not, since no Parliament may make any such law." "No more,"
said Sir Thomas More, as Mr. Rich reported of him, "could
the Parliament make the King supreme head of the Church.'

Upon whose report alone was Sir Thomas More indicted for treason by the statute in which it was made treason to deny that the King was supreme head of the Church, into which indictment were put these words, "maliciously, traitorously, and diabolically."

When Sir Thomas More was brought from the Tower to Westminster Hall to answer the indictment, and was thereupon arraigned at the King's Bench bar before the judges, he openly told them that he would upon that indictment have abided by the law, but that he would thereby have been driven himself to confess the truth of the charge, which was a denial of the King's supremacy. But this, he protested, was untrue, wherefore he pleaded not guilty thereto, and so reserved to himself the advantage to be taken of the body of the accusation after verdict, to avoid that indictment.[38] And, moreover, he added, "if only those odious terms *maliciously, traitorously, and diabolically* were put out of the indictment, he saw nothing therein justly to charge him."

Then for proof to the jury that Sir Thomas More was guilty of this treason, Mr. Rich was called by them to give audience to them, as he did; against whom Sir Thomas More began in this wise to say: "If I were a man, my Lords, that did not regard an oath, I need not, as it is well known, in this place, at this time, or in this case, stand an accused person. And if this oath of yours, Mr. Rich, be true, then I pray I may never see

[38] More was pinning his hopes on a legal technicality, holding still to his position that refusal to take the oath affirming Henry's Supremacy did not legally constitute a denial of it.

God in the face, which I would not say were it otherwise, to win the whole world."

Then he recited the course of all their conversation in the Tower according to the truth, and said, "In faith, Mr. Rich, I am sorrier for your perjury than for my own peril; and you shall understand that neither I nor any man else to my knowledge ever took you to be a man of such credit as in any matter of importance I or any other would at any time vouchsafe to converse with you. And, as you know, I have been acquainted with you and your conversation no small while, for I have known you from your youth. For we long dwelt in one parish together, where, as yourself can tell—I am sorry you compel me so to say—you were esteemed very light of your tongue, a great dicer, and not of commendable fame. And so in your house at the Temple, where your chief bringing up has been, you were likewise accounted.

"Can it therefore seem likely unto your honorable Lordships, that I would in so weighty a cause, so far overshoot myself as to trust Mr. Rich (a man always reputed by me as one of so little truth, as your Lordships have heard) so far above my sovereign Lord the King, or any of his noble councilors, that I would to him utter secrets of my conscience touching the King's supremacy, the special point and only statement so long sought for at my hands? A thing which I never did, nor ever would, after the Statute made thereof, reveal either to the King's Highness himself or to any of his honorable councilors, who were, as it is not unknown to your House, at sundry times and separately, sent from his Grace's own person to the Tower to me for no other purpose. Can this in your judgments, my Lords, seem likely to be true? And if I had so done indeed, my Lords, as Mr. Rich has sworn, seeing it was spoken but in familiar secret talk, nothing affirming, and only imagining cases, without other displeasing circumstances, it cannot justly be taken to be spoken maliciously. And where there is no malice there can be no offense.

"And besides this, I can never think, my Lords, that so many worthy bishops, so many honorable personages, and other worshipful, virtuous, wise, and well-learned men, as at the making of that law were assembled in Parliament, ever meant to have any man punished by death, in whom there could be found no malice, taking *malitia pro malevolentia*.[39] For if *malitia* is generally taken for sin, no man is there then that can thereof acquit himself. *Quia si dixerimus quod peccatum non habemus, nosmetipsos seducimus, et veritas in nobis non est*.[40] And only this word *maliciously* is material in the Statute, as the term *forcible* is in the statute of forcible entries; by which statute if a man enter peaceably, and do not put his adversary out forcibly, it is no offense, but if he put him out forcibly, then by that statute it is an offense.[41] And so shall he be punished under this term *forcible*. Besides this, there is the manifold goodness of my sovereign Lord the King's Highness him-

39 That is, "taking malice to mean ill will."

40 "If we say we have no sin, we fool ourselves and the truth is not in us."

41 The Statute of Forcible Entries declared it illegal to take possession of houses or lands by violence and force of arms. It was a good illustration to use; for violations of the statute were most common, and it would be a familiar example to any group.

self, who has been in so many ways my singular good Lord and Gracious Sovereign, that has so dearly loved me and trusted me even at my first coming into his noble service with the dignity of his honorable Privy Council, vouchsafing to admit me to offices of great credit and worship, and has most liberally advanced me, and finally of his incomparable benignity honored and exalted me for the space of twenty years and more with the weighty office of his Grace's high chancellorship (the like whereof he never did to layman before) next to his own royal person the highest office in this noble realm, so far above my merits or qualities able and meet therefore, showing his continual favor towards me for the space of twenty years and more; and, until at my own poor suit, it pleased his Highness to give me license, with his Majesty's favor, to bestow the residue of my life wholly for the provision of my soul in the service of God and of his special goodness to discharge and unburden me therefrom, he most benignly heaped honors more and more upon me. All this his Highness' goodness, I say, so long continued towards me, were, in my mind, my Lords, matters sufficient to convince you of the slanderous nature of this surmise so wrongfully imagined by this man against me."

Mr. Rich seeing himself so disproved, and his credit so foully defaced, caused Sir Richard Southwell and Mr. Palmer, who at the time of their conversation were in the chamber, to be sworn as to what words passed betwixt them. Whereupon Mr. Palmer in his deposition said that he was so busy about bundling up Sir Thomas More's books in a sack that he paid no heed to their talk. Sir Richard Southwell likewise in his deposition said that because he was appointed only to look to the conveyance of his books, he gave no ear to them. After this, there were many other reasons, not now in my remembrance, alleged by Sir Thomas More in his own defense, to the discredit of the aforesaid evidence of Mr. Rich, and as proof of the clearness of his own conscience.

All of which notwithstanding, the jury found him guilty, and immediately upon the verdict the Lord Chancellor—Chief Commissioner for the case—began to give judgment against him. But Sir Thomas More said to him, "My Lord, when I was engaged in the law, the custom in such a case was to ask the prisoner before judgment, why judgment should not be given against him." Whereupon the Lord Chancellor, staying his judgment, wherein he had partly proceeded, demanded of him what he was able to say against it. Who then in this fashion mildly made answer:

"My Lord," quoth he, "forasmuch as this indictment is grounded upon an Act of Parliament, directly repugnant to the laws of God and his holy Church, the supreme government of which, or of any part thereof, no temporal prince may presume by any law to take upon him, as rightfully it belongs to the See of Rome, a spiritual pre-eminence by the mouth of our Saviour himself, personally present upon the earth, granted to St. Peter and his successors, bishops of the same See, by special prerogative. It is therefore in law amongst Christian men insufficient as a ground for accusing any Christian."

And for proof thereof, amongst divers other reasons and

authorities, he declared that this realm, being but one member and a small part of the Church, might not make a particular law different from the general law of Christ's holy
Catholic Church, any more than the City of London, being
but one poor member in comparison with the whole realm,
might make a law against an Act of Parliament to bind the
whole realm. And, further, he showed that it was contrary both
to the laws and statutes of this land, yet unrepealed, as they
might plainly perceive in Magna Charta, *"Quod Ecclesia An-
glicana libera sit et habeat omnia jura sua integra, et libertates
suas illaesas,"* [42] and contrary to that sacred oath which the
King's Highness himself, and every other Christian prince always took at their coronations. He alleged, moreover, that no
more might this realm of England refuse obedience to his
natural father. For as St. Paul said to the Corinthians, "I have
begottten you, my children in Christ," so might St. Gregory,
Pope of Rome, from whom by St. Augustine his messenger we
first received the Christian faith, truly say of us Englishmen,
"You are my children, because I have given you everlasting salvation, a far better inheritance than any carnal father
can leave unto his child, and by spiritual generation have made
you my spiritual children in Christ."

Then was answer made thereto by the Lord Chancellor, that,
seeing all the bishops, universities, and best learned men of the
realm had agreed to this Act, it was much marveled that he
alone would so stiffly hold out and vehemently argue against

42 "—that the English Church should be free and have all its rights untouched
and its liberties unimpaired."

them all. To that Sir Thomas More replied saying, "If the number of bishops and universities is so material, as your Lordship seems to take it, then I see little cause, my Lords, why that should make any change in my conscience. For I do not doubt that though not in this realm, yet abroad in Christendom they are not the smallest part who are of my mind therein. And if I should speak of those that are already dead, of whom many are now saints in heaven, I am very sure it is the far greater part of them that all the while they lived thought on this matter the way that I think now. And therefore I am not bound, my Lords, to conform my conscience to the council of one realm against the General Council of Christendom."

Now when Sir Thomas More, for voiding the indictment, had taken as many exceptions as he thought meet and alleged more reasons than I can now remember, the Lord Chancellor, loth to have the burden of the judgment wholly depend on himself, openly asked the advice of Lord Fitz-James, then Lord Chief Justice of the King's Bench, and joined in commission with him, whether this indictment were sufficient or not. Who, like a wise man, answered, "My Lords all, by St. Julian"—that was ever his oath—"I must needs confess, that if the Act of Parliament is not unlawful, then by my conscience the indictment is not insufficient." Whereupon the Lord Chancellor said to the rest of the Lords, "Lo, my Lords, lo, you hear what my Lord Chief Justice says," and so immediately gave judgment against him.

After which, the commissioners yet courteously offered, if he had anything else to allege for his defense, to grant him favorable audience. But he answered, "I have not more to say, my Lords, but like as the blessed Apostle St. Paul, who as we read in the Acts of the Apostles, was present and consented to the death of St. Stephen, and kept the clothes of those who stoned him to death, and yet they are now both holy saints in heaven, and shall continue there friends forever, so I verily trust and shall therefore right heartily pray, that though your Lordships have now on earth been judges to my condemnation, we may yet hereafter in heaven all merrily meet together to our everlasting salvation." This much touching Sir Thomas More's arraignment, being not thereat present myself, I have from the credible report of Sir Anthony Sumtleger, Knight, and in part of Sir Richard Heywood, and John Webb, Gentleman, with others of good credit, themselves present at the hearing thereof, as far forth as my poor wit and memory would serve me, here truly related to you.

Now after this arraignment he departed from the bar to the Tower again, led by Sir William Kingston, a tall, strong, and comely knight, Constable of the Tower, his very dear friend, who, when he had brought him from Westminster to the Old Swan towards the Tower, there with a heavy heart, the tears running down his cheeks, bade him farewell. Sir Thomas More seeing him so sorrowful, comforted him with as good words as he could, saying, "Good Mr. Kingston, trouble not yourself, but be of good cheer. For I will pray for you, and my good lady your wife, that we may meet in heaven together, where we shall be merry for ever and ever." Soon afterward, Sir William Kingston, talking with me of Sir Thomas More, said, "In faith, Mr. Roper, I was ashamed of myself, that at my departure from your father, I found my heart so feeble and his so strong, that he was constrained to comfort me who should rather have comforted him."

When Sir Thomas More came from Westminster to the Tower again, his daughter, my wife, desirous to see her father, whom she thought she would never see in this world again, and also to have his final blessing, waited about the Tower wharf, where she knew he would pass by, ere he could enter the Tower. There tarrying for his coming home, as soon as she saw him, after reverently on her knees receiving his blessings, she, hastening forward, without consideration or care of herself, pressing in among the midst of the throng and the Company of the Guard, that with halberts and bills were round about him, hastily ran to him, and there openly in the sight of them all embraced and clasped him about the neck and kissed him. He, well liking her most daughterly love and affection towards him, gave her his fatherly blessing, and many godly words of comfort besides. But after she had parted from him, not satisfied with the sight she had had of her dear father, and having respect neither to herself nor to the press of the people and the multitude that were about him, she suddenly turned back again, and ran to him as before, clasped him about the neck, and divers times together most lovingly kissed him. Then at last, with a full heavy heart she was constrained to part from him; the beholding of which was to many of them that were present so lamentable that it made them for very sorrow mourn and weep.

So remained Sir Thomas More in the Tower more than a sevennight [43] after his judgment. From whence, the day before his execution, he sent his shirt of hair, not willing to have it seen, to my wife, his dearly beloved daughter, and a letter, written with a coal,[44] contained in the aforesaid book of his works, plainly expressing the fervent desire he had to suffer on the morrow, in these words: "I trouble you, good Margaret, much, but I would be sorry if it should be any longer than tomorrow. For tomorrow is St. Thomas' Eve [45] and the Octave of St. Peter,[46] and therefore tomorrow that is a day very meet and convenient for me I long to go to God. And I never liked your manner better than when you kissed me last. For I like it when daughterly love and dear charity have no leisure to look out for worldly courtesy."

And so upon the next morning, being Tuesday, St. Thomas' Eve, and the Octave of St. Peter, in the year of our Lord 1535, according as he in his letter the day before had wished, early

[43] Roper is again slightly in error. It was five days, not seven, between the judgment and the execution.

[44] See More's letter, p. 310.

[45] More could not know that the festival of his beloved St. Thomas, the martyred Becket, would itself soon be brought to an end. In the year following his death, royal orders were issued against all "superfluous" holidays that fell in term time or harvest time. The festival of the martyrdom, falling on December 29, was kept; but the more popular festival of the translation of the relics, coming as it did in harvest time, July 7, was formally abolished in 1538. Like other Saints' Days that were officially dropped, however, it continued to be celebrated in country districts, and as late as 1940 was being observed in a section of rural Somerset.

[46] The Octave was the eighth day, counting the festival day itself, after any church festival. St. Peter's Day was June 29; hence the Octave of St. Peter was July 6. More was executed July 6, 1535.

in the morning there came to him Sir Thomas Pope, his personal friend, with a message from the King and his Council, that he should before nine of the clock in the same morning suffer death, and that therefore he should prepare himself. "Mr. Pope," said he, "for your good tidings I most heartily thank you. I have been always much bounden to the King's Highness for the benefits and honors which he has from time to time most bountifully heaped upon me; and yet more bounden I am to his Grace for putting me into this place, where I have had convenient time and space to have remembrance of my end. And, so help me God, most of all, Mr. Pope, am I bound to his Highness, that it has pleased him so shortly to rid me of the miseries of this wretched world. And therefore will I not fail most earnestly to pray for his Grace, both here and also in another world."

"The King's pleasure is further," quoth Mr. Pope, "that at your execution you shall not speak many words." "Mr. Pope," quoth he, "you do well that you give me warning of his Grace's pleasure. For otherwise I had purposed at that time to have spoken somewhat, but of no matter wherewith his Grace, or any other, should have had cause to be offended. Nevertheless, whatever I had intended, I am ready obediently to conform myself to his Grace's commandment. And I beseech you, good Mr. Pope, to be a mediator to his Highness, that he may permit my daughter Margaret to be present at my burial."

"The King is well contented already," quoth Mr. Pope, "that your wife, children, and other friends shall have free liberty to be present thereat." "Oh, how much beholden," then said Sir Thomas More, "am I to his Grace, that for my poor burial vouchsafeth to have so gracious consideration!" Wherewithal Mr. Pope, taking his leave of him, could not refrain from weeping, which Sir Thomas More perceiving, comforted him in this wise: "Quiet yourself, good Mr. Pope, and be not disconsolate. For I trust that we shall again in heaven see each other full merrily, where we shall be sure to live and love together in joyful bliss eternally."

Upon his departure, Sir Thomas More, as one that had been invited to a solemn feast, changed himself into his best apparel; which Mr. Lieutenant espying advised him to put it off, saying that he who would have it was but a worthless fellow. "What, Mr. Lieutenant," quoth he, "shall I count him a worthless fellow that will do me this day so singular a benefit? Nay, I assure you, were it cloth of gold, I would count it well bestowed on him, as St. Cyprian did,[47] who gave thirty pieces of gold." And albeit at length, through Mr. Lieutenant's persuasions, he altered his apparel, yet, after the example of that holy martyr, St. Cyprian, he did of that little money that was left him, send one angel of gold to his executioner.

And so was he brought by Mr. Lieutenant out of the Tower, and from thence led towards the place of execution, where, going up to the scaffold, which was so weak that it was ready to fall, he said to Mr. Lieutenant, "I pray you, I pray you, Mr. Lieutenant, see me safe up, and for my coming down let me shift for myself." Then he desired all the people thereabouts to pray for him, and to bear witness with him, that he would suffer death

[47] Renowned Bishop of Carthage who was martyred in 258 A.D.

in and for the faith of the holy Catholic Church. Which done, he kneeled down, and after his prayers were said, turned to the executioner, and with a cheerful countenance spoke to him. "Pluck up thy spirits, man, and be not afraid to do thine office. My neck is very short. Take heed therefore thou strike not awry for saving thine honor." So passed Sir Thomas More out of this world to God upon the very same day which himself had most desired.

Soon afterward there came information of his death to the Emperor Charles, who thereupon sent for Sir Thomas Eliott,[48] our English ambassador, and said to him, "My Lord Ambassador, we understand that the King your master has put his faithful servant and grave wise councilor Sir Thomas More to death." Whereto Sir Thomas Eliott answered that he had heard nothing thereof. "Well," said the Emperor, "it is very true; and this we will say, that if we had been master of such a servant, of whose doings we these many years have had no small experience, we would rather have lost the best city in our dominions than such a worthy councilor." Which saying was by Sir Thomas Eliott to myself, my wife, Mr. Clement and his wife, Mr. John Haywood and his wife, and divers others of his friends accordingly reported.

---

[48] This is the Sir Thomas Eliott (more often spelled Elyot) who wrote the *Boke Called the Governour,* and under the influence of Erasmus and other humanist scholars, made several important translations from Greek works.

Roper lists the witnesses who heard Eliott's words, so it seems likely that there is some foundation for this story; but it must have been of an earlier date, referring to some former occasion; for the only known embassy of Eliott to Charles V was in 1531-32, some years before More's death.

LETTERS OF MORE AND MARGARET

LETTERS OF SIR THOMAS MORE AND
HIS DAUGHTER MARGARET

Thanks to the many letters of Erasmus with allusions to the More household; to Holbein's famous drawing of the family group—presumably the basis for a painting that was never made or that has been lost; to Roper's intimate biography of More; and to his own letters, we possess an unusually rich store of knowledge concerning the personal life and family relationships of Sir Thomas More.

The household at Chelsea where the family lived during the most important years of More's life housed not only Sir Thomas, Dame Alice his wife, and their four children, Margaret, Elizabeth, Cecily, and John; but also Alice Middleton, the daughter of Dame Alice by a former marriage, and several other young people, both boys and girls, all of whom grew up as members of one family. All were recipients of the affection and counsel that the head of the house lavished upon his own children, and all shared in their educations and activities. More had advanced ideas on education, particularly the education of women, and the proficiency gained by his daughters in classical learning was a matter of comment among his friends.

More was devoted to all the members of his household, but

his eldest daughter, Margaret, who became the wife of William Roper, More's biographer, appears to have been nearest and dearest to him. The letters here printed passed between the father and daughter during More's last imprisonment in the Tower in the spring and summer of 1535. They show not only the relationship between the two, but are revealing as well of much that was close to the heart and mind of More during the last weeks that he lived. After he had been in prison for a month, Margaret gained the King's permission to visit him. The letters were sent between these visits. The last letter by More was written the day before his execution.

LETTER I

Sir Thomas More's letter to his daughter, Mrs. Margaret Roper, on his first being made prisoner in the Tower of London, on Friday the 17th day of April, 1535.

HEN I WAS before the Lords at Lambeth, I was the first that was called in, albeit Master Doctor, the vicar of Croydon, had come before me, and divers others. After the cause of my sending for was declared unto me (whereof I somewhat marveled in my mind, considering that they sent for no other layman but me), I desired the sight of the Oath, which they showed me under the great seal. Then I desired the sight of the Act of Succession, which was delivered to me in a printed roll. After which read secretly by myself, and the Oath considered with the Act, I showed them that my purpose was not to find any fault, either in the Act or any man that made it, or in the Oath or any man that swore it, nor to condemn the conscience of any other man. But as for myself, in good faith my conscience so moved me in the matter that though I would not refuse to swear to the succession, yet to that Oath that there was offered me, I could not swear without the jeopardizing of my soul to perpetual damnation. And that if they doubted whether I did refuse the Oath only for the grudge of my conscience, or for any other fantasy, I was ready therein to satisfy them by my oath. Which if they trusted not, what should they be the better to give me any oath. And if they trusted that I would therein swear true, then trusted I that of their goodness they would not move me to swear the Oath that they offered me, perceiving that to swear it was against my conscience.

Unto this my Lord Chancellor [1] said that they were all very sorry to hear me say this, and see me thus refuse the Oath. And they all said that on their faith I was the very first that ever refused it; which would cause the King's Highness to conceive great suspicion of me, and great indignation toward me. And therewith they showed me the roll, and let me see the names of the Lords and the Commons who had sworn and subscribed their names already. Which notwithstanding, when they saw that I refused to swear the same myself, though not blaming any other man that had sworn, I was in conclusion commanded to go down into the garden. And thereupon I tarried in the old burned chamber that looks into the garden, and would not go down because of the heat. In that time I saw Master Doctor Latimer [2] come into the garden, and there walked he with

---

[1] It will be remembered from Roper's account (p. 244) that Lord Audley was More's successor in the Chancellorship. Audley had for some time been the King's submissive servant. Now, as Lord Chancellor, he presided over the trials of More and Fisher.

[2] Hugh Latimer is best known as a great Reformation preacher. As a young man he was an ardent champion of the old faith, but by 1529 his preaching had gone so far in the direction of reform that he was involved in conflict with the orthodox prelates. When the King learned that Latimer favored his cause in the divorce question, he came to his rescue on various occasions. After Cranmer was made Archbishop, Latimer was shown special favor and participated in formulating the legislation that led to the separation from Rome.

divers other doctors and chaplains of my Lord of Canterbury.[3]
And very merry I saw him, for he laughed, and took one or
twain about the neck so handsomely that if they had been
women, I would have thought he had waxed wanton. After that
came Master Doctor Wilson [4] forth from the Lords, and was
with two gentlemen brought along with me, and sent straight
to the Tower. What time my Lord of Rochester [5] was called
in before them, that can I not tell. But at night I heard that he
had been before them; but where he remained that night, and
so forth, till he was sent hither, I never heard.

I heard also that Master Vicar of Croydon,[6] and all the
remnant of the priests of London that were sent for, were
sworn; and that they had such favor at the Council's hand that
they were not made to linger, nor to dance any long attendance
to their travail and cost, as suitors were sometime wont to be,
but were sped apace to their great comfort; so for that Master
Vicar of Croydon, either for gladness or for dryness, or else

---

[3] Cranmer was made Archbishop of Canterbury in 1533.

[4] Dr. Nicholas Wilson, chaplain and confessor to the King, had, like More,
been unable to comply with the divorce settlement. A week before the arrest
of More and Fisher he was sent to the Tower for not taking the oath in support
of the Succession. Unlike More and Fisher, however, he later changed his position,
took the oath (1537), and received the King's pardon.

[5] John Fisher, Bishop of Rochester, and Thomas More had been friends for
many years. Like both More and Erasmus, he worked for reform, but within
the framework of the old doctrine. The credence he gave to the imposture of the
Maid of Kent (p. 249) is a blot on an otherwise high reputation.

[6] Rowland Philips, famed as a preacher, became Vicar of Croydon in 1522.
Tradition has it that he was the one who wanted to go as a bishop to Utopia;
see p. 8.

that it might be seen, *Quod ille notus erat pontifici,*[7] went to my Lord's buttery bar, and called for a drink, and drank *valde familiariter.*[8]

When they had played their pageant, and were gone out of the place, then was I called in again. And then was it declared to me what a number had sworn, since I went aside, and gladly without any sticking. Whereat I laid no blame in no man, but for my own self I answered as before. Now as well as before, they somewhat laid unto me for obstinacy, in that, as before, since I refused to swear, I would not declare any special part of that Oath that grudged my conscience, and open the cause wherefore. For thereunto I had said to them that I feared lest the King's Highness would, as they said, take displeasure enough toward me, for the refusal of the Oath only. And that if I should open and disclose the causes why, I should therewith but further exasperate his Highness, which I would in no wise do, but rather would I endure all the danger and harm that might come to me than give his Highness any occasion of further displeasure, than the offering of the Oath of pure necessity constrained me.

Howbeit when they divers times imputed this to me for stubbornness and obstinacy, that I would neither swear the Oath, nor yet declare the causes why, I yielded thus far to them; that rather than be accounted obstinate, I would, upon the King's gracious license, or rather his commandment, as might be my sufficient warrant that my declaration should not offend his

[7] That he was a friend of the Archbishop.
[8] Very familiarly.

Highness nor put me in danger of any of his statutes, be content to declare the causes in writing, and above that to give an oath in the beginning that if I should find those causes by any man answered in such wise as I might think my own conscience satisfied, I would after that with all my heart swear the principal Oath too.

To this I was answered that though the King would give me license under his letters patent, yet would it not serve to protect me against the statute. Whereto I said, that yet if I had them, I would stand unto the trust of his honor at my peril for the remnant. 'But yet,' thought I, 'lo, if I may not declare the causes without peril, then to leave them undeclared is no obstinacy.' My Lord of Canterbury taking hold on what I said, that I condemned not the consciences of them that swore, said to me that it well appeared that I did not take it for a very sure and certain thing that I might not lawfully swear, but rather for a thing uncertain and doubtful. "But then," said my Lord, "you know for a certainty, and a thing without doubt, that you are bound to obey your sovereign Lord your King. And therefore you are bound to leave off the doubts of your unsure conscience in refusing the Oath, and take the sure way in obeying your prince, and swear it." Now it all was so, that in my own mind methought myself not concluded, yet this argument seemed to me suddenly so subtle, and with such authority coming out of so noble a prelate's mouth, that I could again answer nothing thereto, but only that I thought myself I might not well do so, because in my conscience this was one of the cases in which I was not bound that I should obey my prince, since whatsoever other folk thought in the matter (whose conscience or learning I would not condemn nor take upon me to judge), yet in my conscience the truth seemed on the t'other side. Wherein I had not informed my conscience either suddenly or slightly, but by long leisure and diligent search in the matter. And of truth if that reason may conclude, then have we a ready way to avoid all perplexities. For in whatsoever matter the doctors stand in great doubt, the King's commandment given on whitherside he chooses absolves all the doubts.

Then said my Lord of Westminster [9] to me, that howsoever the matter seemed to my own mind, I had cause to fear that my own mind was erroneous, when I saw the Great Council of the realm determine the contrary of my mind, and that therefore I ought to change my conscience. To that I answered, that if there were no more but myself upon my side, and the whole Parliament upon the t'other, I would be sore afraid to lean to my own mind only against so many. But on the other hand, if it so be that in some things, for which I refuse the Oath, I have (as I think I have) upon my part as great a Council and a greater too, I am not then bound to change my conscience and conform it to the Council of one realm against the general Council of Christendom. Upon this, Master Secretary,[10] as he that tenderly favored me, said and swore a great oath, that he had sooner that his only son (who is of truth a goodly young gentleman,

[9] William Benson who was one of the learned doctors to whom the University of Cambridge referred the question of the validity of the King's marriage with Katherine. In 1534, along with other councilors, he was chosen to administer the oath in support of the Succession.

[10] Thomas Cromwell, see p. 247.

and shall, I trust, come to much worship) had lost his head than that I should thus have refused the Oath. For surely the King's Highness would now conceive a great suspicion against me, and think that the matter of the nun [11] of Canterbury was all contrived by my means. To which I said that the contrary was true and well known. And whatsoever should mishap me, it lay not in my power to help it without the peril of my soul.

Then did my Lord Chancellor repeat before me my refusal to Master Secretary, as to one that was going to the King's Grace. And in the rehearsing, his Lordship repeated again that I denied not but was content if I might see my oath on that point framed in such a manner as might stand with my conscience. Then said my Lord: "Marry, Master Secretary, mark that too; that he will not swear that either, but under some certain manner!" "Verily, no, my Lord," quoth I, "but I will see it made in such wise first that I myself may see that I shall neither be foresworn nor swear against my conscience. Surely, as to swearing to the succession I see no peril. (But I thought and do think it reason that to my own oath I look well myself, and have counsel also in the wording; and never intended to swear to a piece and set my hand to the whole Oath.) Howbeit, so help me God, as touching the whole Oath I never withdrew any man from it, nor ever advised any to refuse it, nor never put, nor will put, any scruple in any man's head, but leave every man to his own conscience. And methinks in good faith that so it were good reason that every man should leave me to mine."

11 See p. 249, footnote 26.

LETTER II

Another letter of Sir Thomas More to his daughter, Mrs. Margaret Roper, written with a coal.[12]

MINE OWN good daughter, our Lord be thanked, I am in good health, and in good quiet of mind; and of worldly things I no more desire than I have. I beseech Him make you all merry in the hope of Heaven. And such things as I somewhat longed to talk of with you all, concerning the world to come, our Lord put them into your minds, as I trust He doth, and better too, by His Holy Spirit; who bless you and preserve you all. Written with a coal by your tender loving father, who in his poor prayers forgetteth none of you all, nor your babes, nor your nurses, nor your good husbands, nor your good husbands' shrewd wives, nor your father's shrewd wife neither, nor our other friends. And thus fare ye heartily well, for lack of paper.

Thomas More, Knight.

[12] A piece of charcoal, frequently used when better writing materials were not available.

LETTER III

A third letter of Sir Thomas More to his daughter, Mrs. Margaret Roper, in answer to a letter of hers entreating him to take the Oath of Succession.

UR LORD bless you.

If I had not been, my dearly beloved daughter, at a firm and fast point, I trust, in God's great mercy, this good while before, your lamentable letter had not a little disturbed me, far surely above all other things, of which I hear divers times not a few terrible to me. But surely they all never touched me so near, nor were so grievous to me, as to see you, my well-beloved child, in such vehement, piteous manner, laboring to persuade me of the thing wherein I have, of pure necessity for respect to my own soul, so often given you so precise answer before. Thereto as touching the points of your letter, I can make no answer. For I doubt not but you well remember that the matters which move my conscience (without declaration whereof I can nothing touch the point), I have sundry times told you that I will disclose them to no man. And, therefore, daughter Margaret, I can in this thing go no further, but, like as you labor me again to follow your mind, to desire and pray you both again, to leave off such labor, and with my former answers to hold yourself content.

A deadly grief to me and much more deadly than to hear of mine own death (for the fear thereof, I thank our Lord, the fear of hell, the hope of heaven, and the passion of Christ, daily more and more assuage) is that I perceive my good son your husband, and you, my good daughter, and my good wife, and my other children and innocent friends, in great displeasure and danger of great harm thereby. The prevention whereof, while it lieth not in my hand, I can no further but commit all to God. *Nam in manu dei,* saith the Scripture, *cor regis est, et sicut divisiones aquarum quocunque voluerit impellit illud.*[13] Whose high goodness I most humbly beseech to incline the noble heart of the King's Highness to the tender favor of you all, and to favor me no better than God and myself know that my faithful heart toward him and my daily prayer for him do deserve. For surely if his Highness might inwardly see my true mind such as God knoweth it is, it would, I trust, soon assuage his high displeasure. Which while I can in this world never in such wise show, but that his Grace may be persuaded to believe the contrary of me, I can no further go, but put all in the hands of Him for fear of whose displeasure, for the safeguard of my soul, stirred by mine own conscience (without laying calumny or reproach to any other man's) I suffer and endure this trouble. Out of which I beseech Him to bring me, when His will shall be, into His endless bliss of Heaven, and in the meanwhile give me grace, and you both, in all our agonies and troubles, devoutly to resort prostrate unto the remembrance of that bitter

[13] "The King's heart is in the hand of the Lord, as the rivers of water: he turneth it whithersoever he will." (Proverbs, XXI, 1.)

agony, which our Saviour suffered before His passion on the Mount. And if we diligently do so, I verily trust we shall find therein great comfort and consolation. And thus, my dear daughter, the blessed spirit of Christ, for his tender mercy, govern and guide you all, to His pleasure and your well being and comforts, both body and soul.

Your tender loving Father,
Thomas More, Knight.

LETTER IV

To this last letter Mistress Margaret Roper wrote an answer and sent it to Sir Thomas More her father, the copy whereof here follows.

𝕸INE OWN good father: It is to me no little comfort, since I cannot talk with you by such means as I would like, at the least way to delight myself in this bitter time of your absence by such means as I may, by as often writing to you as shall be expedient, and by reading again and again your most fruitful and delectable letter, the faithful messenger of your very virtuous and spiritual mind, rid from all corrupt love of worldly things and fast knit only in the love of God and desire of Heaven, as becomes a very true worshiper and a faithful servant of God, who I doubt not, good father, holds His holy hand over you, and shall (as He has) preserve you both body and soul (*ut sit mens sana in corpore sano*);[14] and in particular now, when you have rejected all earthly consolations, and resigned yourself willingly, gladly, and fully for His love to His holy protection.

Father, what think you has been our comfort since your departing from us? Surely the experience we have had of your

[14] That you may have a sound mind in a sound body.

past life and godly conversation and wholesome counsel and virtuous example, and a surety not only of the continuance of the same, but also a great increase, by the goodness of our Lord, to the great rest and gladness of your heart, devoid of all earthly dregs and garnished with the noble vesture of heavenly virtues, a pleasant palace for the holy spirit of God to rest in. Who defend you (as I doubt not, good father, but of His goodness He will) from all trouble of mind and of body, and give me, your most loving obedient daughter and handmaid, and all us your children and friends, to follow that we praise in you, and to our only comfort remember and speak together of you, that we may in conclusion meet with you, my own dear father, in the bliss of Heaven, to which our most merciful Lord has brought us with His precious blood.

Your own most loving obedient daughter and bedeswoman,[15] who desires above all worldly things to be in John a-Wood's [16] stead to do you some service. But we live in hope that we shall shortly receive you again. I pray God heartily we may, if it be His holy will.

Margaret Roper.

[15] A term of respect as "your humble servant."
[16] More's personal servant who attended him in the Tower. See p. 260.

LETTER V

A letter written and sent by Sir Thomas More to his daughter Mistress Roper, written the second or third day of May, in the year of our Lord 1535, and in the 27th year of the reign of King Henry VIII.

OUR LORD bless you.

My dearly beloved daughter, I doubt not but by reason of the King's councilors resorting hither at this time, in which (our Lord be their comfort) these fathers of the Charterhouse and Master Reynolds of Sion [17] have now been sentenced to death for treason (whose matters and causes I know not) you mayhap are put in trouble and fear of mind concerning me being prisoner here, specially since it is not unlikely that you have heard that I was brought also before the council here myself. I have thought it necessary to inform you of the very truth, to the end that you should neither conceive more hope than the matter gives, lest on another turn it might aggrieve

---

[17] See p. 264. Reynolds and his fellow-monks, who had also denied the Supremacy, were sent to the Tower and tried and sentenced only a few days before More wrote this letter. At the trial, Reynolds spoke much in the vein used by More two months later, appealing to the past history of the Church and to the wider body of the Church outside of England. They were executed on May 4th at Tyburn.

your sorrow; nor more grief and fear than the matter gives on the t'other side.

Wherefore, briefly you shall understand that on Friday, the last day of April, in the afternoon, Master Lieutenant [18] came in here to me, and told me that Master Secretary would speak with me, whereupon I shifted my gown, and went out with Master Lieutenant into the gallery to him, where I met many, some known and some unknown, in the way. And in conclusion coming into the chamber where his Mastership sat with Master Attorney, Master Solicitor, Master Bedell, and Master Doctor Tregonwell,[19] I was invited to sit down with them, which in no wise I would. Whereupon Master Secretary said to me that he doubted not but that I had, by such friends as hither had resorted to me, seen the new statutes made at the last sitting of the Parliament. Whereunto I answered: "Yea, verily. Howbeit, forasmuch as, being here, I have no conversation with any people, I thought it little need for me to bestow much time upon them, and therefore I returned the book shortly, and the effect of the statutes I never marked or studied to put in remembrance." Then he asked me whether I had not read the *first* statute of them, of the King being Head of the Church. Where-

---

[18] Sir Edmund Walsingham, who occupied a house within the precincts of the Tower and had personal charge of the prisoners. He was appointed to the office in 1525 and held it for twenty-five years. More was one of many eminent persons who came under his charge.

[19] Master Attorney, Sir Christopher Hales; Master Solicitor, Richard Rich; Master Bedell, Thomas Bedyl, Clerk of the Privy Council; Master Doctor Tregonwell, Judge of the Admiralty. All were Privy Councillors chosen to carry on the examinations of More and Fisher.

unto I answered, "Yes." Then his Mastership declared unto me
that since it was now by act of Parliament ordained that his
Highness and his heirs are, and ever of right have been, and
perpetually should be, Supreme Head in earth of the Church
of England under Christ, the King's pleasure was that those of
his council there assembled should demand my opinion, and
what my mind was therein. Whereto I answered that in good
faith I had well trusted that the King's Highness would never
command any such question to be demanded of me, considering that I had ever from the beginning well and truly from time
to time declared my mind to his Highness; "and since that
time," I said, "unto your Mastership, Master Secretary, also, both
by mouth and by writing. And now I have in good faith discharged my mind of all such matters, and neither will dispute
kings' titles nor popes'; but the King's true faithful subject I
am and will be, and daily I pray for him, and all his, and for
you all that are of his honorable council, and for all the realm.
And otherwise than this, I never intend to meddle."

Whereto Master Secretary answered that he thought this manner of answer would not satisfy nor content the King's Highness,
but that his Grace would exact a more full answer. And his
Mastership added thereto that the King's Highness was a prince,
not of rigor, but of mercy and pity. And though he had found
obstinacy at some time in certain of his subjects, yet when he
should find them at another time conformable and willing to
submit themselves, his Grace would show mercy: and that concerning myself, his Highness would be glad to see me take such
comfortable ways that I might be abroad in the world again

among other men, as I have been before. Whereto I shortly (after the inward disposition of my mind) answered for very truth, that I would never meddle in the world again, even to have the world given to me. And to the remnant of the matter, I answered in effect as before, showing that I had fully determined with myself neither to study nor meddle with any matter in this world, but that my whole study should be on the passion of Christ, and my own passage out of this world.

Upon this I was commanded to go out for a while, and afterward called in again. At which time Master Secretary said to me that though I were a prisoner condemned to perpetual prison, yet I was not thereby discharged of my obedience and allegiance to the King's Highness. And thereupon he demanded me whether I thought that the King's Grace might not exact of me such things as are contained in the statutes and upon like pains, as he might other men. Whereto I answered that I would not say the contrary. Whereto he said that, likewise as the King's Highness would be gracious to them that he found conformable, so his Grace would follow the course of his laws toward such as he shall find obstinate. And his Mastership said further that my demeanor in that matter was a thing that of likelihood made others so stiff therein as they are. Whereto I answered that I gave no man occasion to hold any point one or other, nor ever gave any man advice or counsel therein one way or other. And for conclusion I could no farther go, whatsoever pain should come thereof. "I am," quoth I, "the King's true faithful subject and daily bedesman, and pray for his Highness and all the realm. I do nobody harm, I say no harm, I think no harm, but wish everybody good. And if this be not enough to keep a man alive, in good faith I long not to live. And I am dying already, and have, since I came here, been divers times in the condition where I thought to die within one hour. And I thank our Lord that I was never sorry for it, but rather sorry when I saw the pang past. And therefore my poor body is at the King's pleasure. Would God my death might do him good!"

After this Master Secretary said: "Well, you find no fault in that statute: find you any in any of the other statutes after it?" Whereto I answered, "Sir, whatever thing should seem to me other than good in any of the other statutes or in that statute either, I would not declare what fault I found, nor speak thereof." Whereto finally his Mastership said, full gently, that no advantage should be taken of anything that I had spoken here. And whether he said farther that there was none to be taken, I do not well remember. But he said that a report should be made unto the King's Highness, and his gracious pleasure known. Whereupon I was delivered again to Master Lieutenant, who was then called in. And so was I by Master Lieutenant brought again into my chamber.

And here I am yet in such condition as I was, neither better nor worse. That which shall follow lies in the hand of God, whom I beseech to put in the King's Grace's mind the thing that may be to his high pleasure, and in mine to mind only the welfare of my soul, with little regard of my body, and you with all yours, and my wife and all my children, and all our other friends, both bodily and spiritually to fare heartily well. And I pray you and them all to pray for me, and take no thought whatever shall happen me. For I verily trust in the goodness of God, seem it never so evil to this world, it shall indeed in another world be for the best.

Your loving father,
Thomas More, Knight.

LETTER VI

Another letter written and sent by Sir Thomas More to his daughter, Mistress Roper, in the year of our Lord 1535, and in the 27th year of the reign of King Henry VIII.

OUR LORD bless you and all yours.

Forasmuch, dearly beloved daughter, as it is likely that you either have heard, or shortly shall hear, that the council were here this day,[20] and that I was before them, I have thought it necessary to send you word how the matter stands, and verily, to be short, I perceive little difference between this time and the last. For as far as I can see, the whole purpose is either to drive me to say precisely the t'one way or t'other. Here sat my Lord of Canterbury, my Lord Chancellor, my Lord of Suffolk,[21] of Lord of Wiltshire,[22] and Master Secretary. And after my coming, Master Secretary made recital in what wise he had reported unto the King's Highness what had been said by his Grace's council to me, and what had been answered by me to them at

20 This was the third of June.
21 Charles Brandon, one of the least worthy of the King's courtiers. He helped to secure the downfall of Wolsey, among others, but feathered his own nest richly, acquiring lands, offices, and wealth.
22 Thomas Boleyn. See above, p. 251, footnote 27.

my other being before them here last. Which thing his Mastership related, in good faith, very well, as I acknowledged and confessed and heartily thanked him therefore. Whereupon he added thereto that the King's Highness was nothing content nor satisfied with my answer, but thought that, by my demeanor, I had been the occasion of much grudge and harm in the realm, and that I had an obstinate and an evil mind toward him, and that my duty was, being his subject (and so he had sent them now in his name to command me upon my allegiance), to make a plain and final answer whether I thought the statute lawful or not. And that I should either acknowledge and confess it lawful, that his Highness should be Supreme Head of the Church of England, or else utter plainly my malignity. Whereto I answered that I had no malignity, and therefore I could utter none. And as to the matter, I could no other answer make than I had before made, which answer his Mastership had there reported. Very heavy I was that the King's Highness should have any such opinion of me. Howbeit, if there were one that had informed his Highness many evil things of me that were untrue, to which his Highness for the time gave credence, I would be very sorry that he should have that opinion of me the space of one day. Howbeit, if I were sure that another would come on the morrow, by whom his Grace should know the truth of my innocency, I should in the meanwhile comfort myself with consideration of that. And likewise now, though it is great heaviness to me that his Highness has such opinion of me for the while, yet have I no remedy to help it, but only comfort myself with this consideration, that I know very well that the time shall come when God shall declare my truth toward his Grace before him and all the world. And whereas that might haply seem to be but a small cause of comfort, because I might take harm here first meanwhile, I thanked God that my cause was such here in this matter, through the clearness of my own conscience, that though I might have pain, I could not have harm. For a man in such a case may lose his head and have no harm. For I was very sure that I had no corrupt affection, but that I had always from the beginning truly accustomed myself to look first upon God, and next upon the King, according to the lesson that his Highness taught me at my first coming to his noble service, the most virtuous lesson that ever prince taught his servant. That his Highness has of me now such opinion is my great heaviness. But I have no means, as I said, to help it, but only comfort myself in the meantime with the hope of that joyful day in which my truth toward him shall well be known. And in this matter further I could not go, nor other answer thereto could I make.

To this it was said by my Lord Chancellor and Master Secretary both that the King might by his laws compel me to make a plain answer thereto, either the t'one way or the t'other. Whereto I answered that I would not dispute the King's authority, what his Highness might do in such a case. But I said that verily, under correction, it seemed to me somewhat hard. For if it so were that my conscience moved me against the statute (wherein how my conscience moves me I make no declaration) then, I, nothing doing and nothing saying against the statute, it were a very hard thing to compel me to say, either precisely with it, against my conscience to the loss of my soul, or precisely against it, to the destruction of my body. To this Master Secretary said that I had ere this when I was Chancellor examined heretics and thieves and other malefactors, and gave me great praise, above my deserving, in that behalf. And he said that I then, as he thought, and at least the bishops, did use to examine heretics, whether they believed the Pope to be the Head of the Church, and used to compel them to make a precise answer thereto. And why should not then the King, since it is a law made here that his Grace is Head of the Church here, compel men to answer precisely to the law here, as they did concerning the Pope?

I answered and said that I protested that I intended not to defend my side, or stand in contention. But I said there was a difference between those two cases, because at that time, as well here as elsewhere through the body of Christendom, the Pope's power was recognized for an undoubted thing; which seems not like a thing agreed in this realm, and the contrary taken for truth in other realms. Whereto Master Secretary answered that men were as well burned for denying that, as they are beheaded for denying this; and therefore as good reason to compel them to make a precise answer to the t'one as to the t'other. Whereto I answered that since in this case a man is not so bound in his conscience by a law of one realm, where there is a law of the whole body of Christendom to the contrary in a matter touching belief, as he is by a law of the whole body, even though there happen to be made in some place a local law to the contrary; the reasonableness or the unreasonable-ness in binding a man to precise answer stands not in the respect or difference between beheading or burning, but, because of the difference in the charge to the conscience, the difference stands between beheading and hell. Much was there answered unto this, both by Master Secretary and my Lord Chancellor, over long to rehearse.

And in conclusion they offered me an oath, by which I should be sworn to make true answer to such things as should be asked me on the King's behalf, concerning the King's own person. Whereto I answered that verily I never purposed to swear any book oath more while I lived. Then they said that I was very obstinate if I would refuse that, for every man does it in the Star Chamber [23] and everywhere. I said that was true, but I had not so little foresight but that I might well conjecture what would be part of my interrogatories; and it was as good to refuse them at the first as afterward. Whereto my Lord Chancellor answered that he thought I guessed truth, for I should see them. And so they were showed me, and they were but two; the first, whether I had seen the statute; the t'other, whether I believed it were a lawful statute or not. Whereupon I refused the oath, said further by mouth that the first I had before confessed, and to the second I would make no answer; which was the end of our conversation, and I was thereupon sent away.

In the conversation before, it was said that they marveled that I should stake so much on my conscience, while at the uttermost

[23] Star Chamber, an ancient high court, consisting of the King's Privy Council or certain members of it, sitting as a court with certain judges to try persons suspected of action against the crown. It was abolished in 1641.

I was not sure therein. Whereto I said that I was very sure that my own conscience, as informed as it is by such diligence as I have so long taken therein, may stand with my own salvation. I meddle not with the conscience of them that think otherwise. Every man *suo damno stat aut cadit*.[24] I am no man's judge. It was also said to me that if I had as lief be out of the world as in it, as I had there said, why did I not then speak plain out against the statute? It well appeared that I was not content to die, though I said so. Whereto I answered, as the truth is, that "I have not been a man of such holy living as I might be bold to offer myself to death, lest God for my presumption might suffer me to fall, and therefore I put not myself forward but to draw back. Howbeit, if God draw me to it Himself, then trust I in His great mercy that He shall not fail to give me grace and strength."

In conclusion Master Secretary said that he liked me this day much worse that he did the last time. For then he said he pitied me much, and now he thought I meant not well. But God and I both know that I mean well, and so I pray God to do by me. I pray you, be you and my other good friends of good cheer, whatsoever befall me, and take no thought for me but pray for me, as I do and shall for you and all them.

Your tender loving Father,
Thomas More, Knight.

[24] Every man to his own damnation stands or falls.

LETTER VII

*Sir Thomas More was beheaded at the Tower-hill,
in London, on Tuesday, the sixth day of July, in the
year of our Lord 1535, and in the 27th year of the
reign of King Henry VIII. And on the day next
before, being Monday, and the fifth day of July, he
wrote with a coal a letter to his daughter Mistress
Roper, and sent it to her (which was the last thing
that ever he wrote), the copy whereof here follows.*

OUR LORD bless you, good daughter, and your good husband and your little boy and all yours, and all my children and all my god-children and all our friends. Recommend
me, when you may, to my good daughter Cecily, whom I beseech our Lord to comfort. And I send her my blessing and all
her children, and pray her to pray for me. I send her a handker-
chief; and God comfort my good son her husband. My good
daughter Dance [25] hath the picture in parchment that you delivered to me from my Lady Coniers; her name is on the back-
side. Show her that I heartily pray her that you may send it in
my name to her again, for a token from me to pray for me. I like

[25] More's second daughter, Elizabeth, wife of William Dauncy. Her husband
sat in the Parliament of 1529.

special well Dorothy Coly,[26] I pray you be good to her. I would like to know whether this is she that you wrote me of. If not, yet I pray you be good to the t'other as you may in her affliction, and to my good daughter Joan Aleyn[27] too. Give her, I pray you, some kind answer, for she sued me hither this day to pray you be good to her. I cumber you, good Margaret, much, but I would be sorry if it should be any longer than tomorrow. For it is Saint Thomas' Eve, and the Utas of Saint Peter:[28] and therefore tomorrow I long to go to God: it were a day very meet and convenient for me. I never liked your manner toward me better than when you kissed me last: for I love when daughterly love and dear charity hath no leisure to look to worldly courtesy. Farewell, my dear child, and pray for me, and I shall for you and all your friends, that we may merrily meet in Heaven. I thank you for your great cost. I send now to my good daughter Clement[29] her algorism stone,[30] and I send her and my godson

[26] Dorothy Coly was maid to Margaret Roper and carried messages for her to her father while he was in the Tower. She later married John Harris, who had been More's secretary and for some years a member of his household. It was through Harris and his wife that many of More's letters were preserved.

[27] The term "daughter" here is one of affection rather than relationship. It appears from the next sentence that she also may have been Margaret Roper's maid.

[28] See p. 277, footnote 45.

[29] Again "daughter" is used as a term of affectionate familiarity. The reference is to Margaret Gigs, one of the young people who grew up in the More household, and became the wife of John Clement, also a protégé of More.

[30] Algorism is a system of computation attributed to an Arabic scholar of the ninth century from whose name the term is derived. It was introduced in the west in the twelfth century and soon replaced Abacus methods in many types of calculation. Algorism stones were apparently counters used in making the calculations.

and all hers God's blessing and mine. I pray you at a time convenient recommend me to my good son John More.[31] I liked well his natural fashion. Our Lord bless him and his good wife, my loving daughter, to whom I pray him to be good, as he hath great cause: and that if the land of mine come to his hand, he break not my will concerning his sister Dance. And our Lord bless Thomas and Austen [32] and all that they shall have.

[31] John More had accompanied his sister Margaret and Margaret Clement to seek his father's blessing when More was returning to the Tower after having received his sentence.

[32] More's grandsons, children of John More.

M8...